CATTLE, COUNTRY and CHAMPIONS

by

Reuben Albaugh

FIRST PRINTING
1971
DAVIS, CALIFORNIA

In Appreciation

The author wishes to thank Drs. G. M. Spurlock, and Howard Dail and his wife Vira for their assistance in organizing and editing the material and Lucy Garcia for typing the manuscript.

Preface

Some of the articles that appear on the following pages will have a familiar ring—having been previously published in leading livestock magazine (Western Livestock Journal and California Cattleman) during the last four decades. The author does not claim to be a genius with pen and words, but has a deep and lasting love for the great western country, and for the friendly, generous, and hospitable people who set it apart from the rest of the great and wonderful world.

Although these stories are steeped in sagebrush flavor, an attempt has been made to depict the importance of the "Land of the Setting Sun" and to capture the philosophies and personalities of the men who wear the Stetson hat, high-heeled boots and the jingling spur. It is hoped that those who peruse these pages will have their interest whetted for the colorful, historical cattle country and that they will find pleasure and gain knowledge when reading about my Champions of the West.

Reuben Albaugh

To My Mother

A native daughter of California
To the very last degree.
You represent this golden state
In all its entirety.

From early west traditions
The pioneer regime
You captured her hospitality
And friendliness supreme.

The Albaugh ranch still stands as when
The west was young and gay
The doors are wide for all who chance
To pass along that way.

From hearty folk of the early west
You learned almost from birth
To cook the food they like so well
To love the rich, black earth.

From them you learned to entertain,
Friend or foe the same
Bring happiness to all you met
No matter from whence they came.

From them you learned to make a dress
To cook and bake as well
To laugh and be good natured
Generous and swell.

At Christmas time each year
Your family gathers 'round
To share the love you radiate
When snow is on the ground.

Salt of the earth of this great land
To us you'll always be
A champion of fine womanhood
Mother supreme to me.

Table of Contents

California's Cattle History

Cattle, grass and water — nature's gifts. Cornwell Ranch, King City, Calif.

Almost four centuries of history's aged and yellow pages must be turned back if one is to review the cattle industry of California, that great state that stretches some 800 miles along the churning water of the mighty Pacific. Cattle followed close on the heels of Cortez in his conquest of Mexico and they accompanied the weary Spanish padres from mission to mission all the way up the Pacific Coast along the El Camino Real, the King's Highway. In no other part of the world does the tradition of great commercial cattle herds reach as far back in history.

Tales of grass and water, ranches and ranchos, the Spanish Don and his golden horse and silver outfit, the vaquero and the hacienda, the rodeos, fiestas and the senoritas protray a life known nowhere else in the world. Under the brilliant and sunny California skies, the manana attitude was easily defended and living was rich and carefree as well as colorful and romantic. There were problems of Indians, thieves and rustlers, of course, and of wars over rights of grass and water. But the gay life of the Spanish-American highlighted those first years of the cattle industry and easily blotted out such trivial difficulties. So we enter the first chapter of California's cattle history in a blaze of color and glory which has been so often captured in song and story, such as "Home on the Range" and "Ramona".

Under the tireless efforts of Father Junipero Serra, the herds belonging to the missions were rapidly expanded. Each mission had it own cattle and the Indians were taught to care for the stock, to make butter and cheese, and to slaughter and care for the meat.

By 1786, one decade after the first mission had been established, about 70,000 head of cattle were reported on California's grassy hills, showing that the industry was well founded. They were mostly of the Longhorn Spanish-American type in an array of colors. They were late maturing, thin of flank, with the speed of a race horse. They were well-equipped to harvest the feed of the times and to take care of themselves in this wild and unsettled country. (Today our Golden State) boasts 5,000,000 head).

This was the era of land grants, which was an established method of colonization used by the Spaniards. At first these lands were granted to the permittee for life's use for raising livestock and to stimulate the business of the country. Later these grants were made legal property, the title of which was upheld in many courts of the land.

Hides and tallow were the main articles of commerce. Meat had little value, which is some contrast to conditions of today when meat is considered the basis of all American meals.

Because of the large herds that running on the open, free range, definite branding laws were established by the Spanish government and were rigidly enforced. Roundup and slaughter dates were announced in advance and such schedules were strictly maintained. It was during these times that the foundation for the rodeos of today were laid. In order to control the killing of too many cattle, a 25 percent per head tax was levied on all cattle slaughtered. It was this system of taxation which paid the cost of government.

Prices of cattle in those days were $4 or $5 per head, for a bull and $2 for a cow. Dried beef sold at 25 pounds for $1.

Meat cut and ready for drying was sold at 31½c for 25

pounds; chopped tallow, $1.12 for 25 pounds; untanned hides, 37c; and tanned hides, $2.25.

The peak era in the first chapter of the cattle industry in California was from 1830 to 1847. All restrictive measures of the government were lifted and trade in hides and tallows was resumed with other countries. This brought about a tremendous boom in this business.

With the discovery of gold in 1848 on the American River by John Sutter's man, John Marshall, the second chapter of the cattle business was started. Previous to this, Sutter had established himself as one of the famous pioneers of California. He had great herds of cattle and acres upon acres of rich range and farming land. History indicates that he was in frequent communication with John Larkin of Monterey, who was a great asset in conducting Sutter's large business affairs.

When the miners of '49 came, eager and restless in seeking the yellow dirt, they had no concern for Sutter's large holdings. They slaughtered his cattle and laid waste to his property, and John Sutter, the founder of the capital of California at Sacramento, died a poor man. Nevertheless, he was truly the great cattleman of this second era.

The cattleman's greatest enemy — drought — entered the picture in a very severe way in 1862. This, together with importations of eastern stock and the entrance of the "gringo" into the business, caused tremendous losses to the industry. This period was one of the greatest depressions in California cattle history.

Following this period came the end of the hide and tallow days, and the cattle industry started on what was called the transition era. Completion of the Transcontinental Railroad in 1869 brought rapid settlement to the West. Cattle movements were made easier and fence laws were inaugurated and enforced.

Barbed wire was invented, making it possible for the farmers and the squatters to fence their lands away from the cattle barons. The windmill was also introduced into the picture, allowing for full utilization of certain dry areas. Both barbed wire and the windmill were as important to the settlement of the West as the cotton gin was to the deep and sunny South.

Homestead law, different from land grants, was instituted. Also timber culture claims were available to land seekers. It was during this area that the government gave rights-of-way to railroads.

All of these changes reduced the great free and open range

area of California by some 30 million acres and started a movement of crowding the cattle back to the hills. This was stopped only recently by the coming of irrigated pastures.

It was during this period that Henry Miller, the butcher boy from Germany, rolled across the scene; and before he laid down his tools in 1914, he had acquired over a million acres of land and owned over a million head of cattle, an accomplishment that could not be equalled in any other country around the world. His practices and methods had great influence on the cattle industry and many other operators copied them and put them to use. His **HH** and wagon wrench irons became famous over California, Oregon, and Nevada.

Every hobo in the land was welcome at Miller's ranches for a handout. They referred to his big cattle camps as "the route of the dirty plate." This was Miller's insurance policy against fire and destruction to his large holdings.

From 1890 to the present time might be considered as the "Chapter of progress, science and education," for it was during this period that much emphasis was placed on better breeding, improved feeding, proper disease control, development of irrigation, better marketing, and range management.

Breed improvement started on the first Mexican cattle in California by crossing them with Durhams or Shorthorns. Later the Herefords were introduced and today the white-face (almost completely) dominate the cattle industry of the state as far as range cattle are concerned. Mexican-type cattle are still to be found in California and are the main stock used for roping events at California rodeos. It was during this span of years that the practice of running steers until they were 4 to 5 years old was discontinued, and cattle were marketed at an earlier age, making a more rapid turnover in the business and supplying more tender, delicious meat to the consumer. Supplementary feeding on the range with cottonseed cake and in the feedlots with barley, milo and beet pulp was introduced and practiced.

Disease control, such as eradication of tuberculosis, was accomplished during this period. Vaccination against anthrax, blackleg and Bang's disease became common practices among the rangemen of this cattle empire.

Irrigated pastures boomed into the picture the latter part of this period and showed evidence of revolutionizing the entire business. Rather high-priced expensive lands, when seeded to proper grasses and legumes, have been found to make large returns when grazed by beef cattle. These lush green pastures are promising tools which the cattlemen plan to use in the future for coping with "Old Man Drought," a frequent visitor to the West.

Brush suppression on the ranges by proper control burning, bulldozing and rolling was introduced to increase the carrying capacity of these areas. Range fertilization, water development, and reseeding were brought into practice and native grasses were favored by the more progressive growers as the University research staff and Extension Service put educational and test plot programs into the field. L. H. Rochford became the first "Extension Specialist in Animal Husbandry" and he together with other Extension men and research workers like Dr. George H. Hart and Professor H. R. Guilbert promoted these improved programs that emphasized more efficiency on the range. Mr. Rochford later became manager of the Tejon Ranch located near Bakersfield, which is said to be one of the largest cattle holdings in California. He is still a member of the board of directors. Harold Thurber, former farm advisor of Imperial County, has assumed the responsibility as manager of the cattle on this empire.

Howard Leach, of Salinas, has recently been employed as over all manager of this huge agricultural empire.

Cooperative marketing had its inception in 1924. This program was sparked by a prominent, smart and fighting cattleman known in all cattle circles as Hub Russell. He, as president of the Western Cattle Marketing Association, and Roy Hagan, an Extension Service worker from the University of California, as secretary, stumped the state for this marketing cause. The organization was predicated on the fact that California imported 25 per cent of her meat and such a program would increase income by selling direct on the home ranch, making for more orderly marketing. Unusual weather conditions coupled with falling prices were the main reasons this plan was discontinued after operating for a few years.

The story of the history of the cattle business in California would not be complete if one did not mention that a real cowman in this state was also a splendid horseman. California cowhorses were known the world over for their working ability on cattle, their handiness, and particularly the soft velvet mouth that they had. This ability to break cow-horses has been handed down from the very early-day cattlemen, when a good cow-horse was the greatest asset a man could have other than a splendid wife.

Instead of exporting hides and tallows as in the days of the Spanish padres, California today imports about 60 per cent of the meat she consumes. This, spliced with the fact that the population in this state is growing rapidly, indicates that the California cattleman will have a home market for his products. Although costs of production will be higher than in most other cattle areas, he will be conducting one of the finest and most interesting businesses known in the field of agriculture. These are some of the predictions that can be made with a high degree of accuracy as this old and colorful business starts on another century of scientific progress.

Half bison, half Hereford cow after 20 calves; 22 years old.
Manyberries Experiment Station, Alberta, Canada.

Courtesy of F. H. Peters

Our Oldest Business

At the waterhole.

Many thrilling chapters of American history have been written around the West, that great portion of our country that lies between the one-hundredth meridian and westward to the Pacific Coast. Roughly, it is that section of the continent that was inhabited by the buffalo, prairie dog, coyote, and the wolf.

Life on the range has been intriguing and colorful, and has attracted many types of people. During the early days when the cattle industry was in the making, a large number of the big outfits were owned by syndicate companies from England.

The basis for many stories of the West have been cattle, cowboys, cow ponies, barbed wire, the windmill, the nester, the six-shooter, the branding iron, and the poker game. Cattle, that magnetic and colorful word of the 18-carat bracket, historically surpasses them all.

The first cattle to survive and reproduce came to the continent in about 1521, and into the U.S. in about 1540. Gregorio de Villalobos was the first cattleman in our western country. Cortez had the first branding iron which was three Christian crosses. The first registered branding iron in California in use today was Alberto Trescony's, grandfather of Julius Trescony, prominent stockman of southern Monterey County. The first cowboys and herdsmen also wore a brand. It was the custom in those days for large landowners to brand their slaves with a "G" on the left jaw which meant "Guerra."

Many Easterners might think that the West is young and raw, but one can see that the cattle industry was well established many years before the British colony was established at Jamestown. Except for fur trapping and mining, it is the oldest industry in our country. It took about 200 years for the country lying from the Atlantic to the Mississippi River to be settled and conquered. But it required only a little over one decade (about 12 years) for the range area of the West to be settled. That occurred from about 1869 to 1882.

Texas is the mother country of "cattleland." It was from this great state that the seedstock of most other western states sprang. So strong was the Texan influence on the cattle industry that even today traditions, language, and methods of handling cattle are extremely southern.

Although the cattleman or westerner lived a reckless, slam-bang life, his word was considered as good as gold, and his manners and hospitality were among the finest in the land. A stranger was always welcome on the range to put up his horse and "spear a bean." This was probably due to the fact that this country was sparsely settled and strangers were a source of news and company.

In the range country, a splendid wife, an outstanding horse, a good dog, a 2 gun fighter, a top cowboy were considered gifts of God. Cattlemen are known far and wide for their tough constitution. They traveled "light," carrying only a change of underwear, a bottle of whiskey, and silk handkerchieves in their black satchels. Jess Cornwell of King City, when asked why he didn't secure a hotel room in Salinas for Big Week, replied, "Who needs a room, it only lasts 4 days." Jess played poker all night and attended the show during the day so he had no time to sleep.

A cattleman everywhere enjoys an enviable social standing Wherever his responsibilities and assignments take him, he is accepted by people in many walks of life. Because of this social status he is very proud of his occupation. This same social prestige attracts people from other industries into the cattle business. There is a saying in the western country, "If you want to make someone feel good, call him a cowboy." With this greeting he is apt to smile and say, "Thanks, partner."

The cattlemen's menu for the entire West consisted of biscuits usually baked in a dutch oven, fried meat, water gravy and dried fruit. The drink was strong black coffee with no sugar or cream. "Buckaroo" coffee was sometimes made by tossing a few handfuls of coffee in a pot of water, and building a fire with sagebrush then bring it to a boil. After boiling for several minutes, an egg shell was thrown in to settle the grounds. Coffee made in this manner is said to be, in many instances, strong enough to float a horseshoe. One of the violations of the range code was to eat beef that carried your own brand. The beef of another man's iron was always sweeter and more nutritious. The philosophy back of this was that since your neighbor ate your beef, things would even out.

The saddle was the most important part of the cowboy's equipment. It means more to him than any other single article. He might go to town and gamble away all his savings, his horse, and many other parts of his equipment, but almost never his saddle. He would rather carry it home on his back. Built around this custom is a saying that when a man's word is no longer good he has "sold his saddle." Or when he had lost his business, this same phrase was heard, in a sympathetic tone. It is not certain who invented the saddle, but the early Spanish pioneers brought it to America. It was probably introduced to Spain by the Moors.

The American saddle has a horn which is used mainly to dally in roping and working cattle. It is also used by cowboys in riding rough horses and when used in this capacity, the habit is known as "choking the biscuit." The saddle has a seat, skirts, latigo, stirrups, and in many instances tapaderos. The kind of a saddle used depended upon the section of the country. In California the center fire rig was used. In Texas, the double rig (two cinches) was popular, and in the Ozark and Flint Hills country, the three-quarter rig predominated.

Chaps, another article of equipment are universally worn whenever cattle are managed. They protect the legs from cold and brush and enable the rider to better grip his saddle. They come in several varieties, such as the bat-winged leather kind, the buckskin tight fitting variety, the chinks also made of buckskin cover only the front of the leg, the goat skin chap with the hair on the outside. These latter leg protectors came in a variety of colors ranging from white to bright orange. They were used mostly in the northern country.

The boots the cowboy wore were always tight fitting. They were highheeled to prevent the foot from slipping through the stirrup. These high heels also prevented the cowhand from slipping when roping and stopping animals while on foot.

The 10 gallon hat the cowboy is supposed to wear today was seldom seen on the range in the early days. Charlie Russell's paintings clearly indicate the northern early-day cattlemen wore a medium-size brim hat with four indentations in the crown The wide brim was used for protection against the sun and other elements. In the brush country, a string was usually fastened in the hat band, which went under the cowboy's chin thus preventing the loss of his sombrero.

A cowboy's rope or "string" had many uses: to lasso animals, pull cattle from the bog, kill rattlesnakes, rescue a man from drowning, mend fences, and hang men.

Early writers of cowboy history refer to the bandana handkerchief, as the flag of the range. It has many uses such as: two handkerchieves tied together made an excellent sling for a broken arm. It was used to dry face and hands, tie around the neck, a blind for a horse, for piggin' string, to protect the nose and throat during dust and blizzards, to wipe off perspiration, to hold handles of hot branding irons, to strain muddy water and to cover the face of a bandit. When a cowboy was killed on the range, it was customary to put his bandana handkerchief over his face and cover him with sod.

Cowboys sang songs while tending the herd for the purpose of keeping them contented, thus preventing stampedes. Upon occasions around the campfire, he would entertain the group with a popular Western Ballad. Other hands who were not fortunate enough to have a singing voice would entertain his buddies with poetry — such as "The Face on the Bar Room Floor," and "The Shooting of Dan McGrew."

Playing cards was one of the great pastimes of cattlemen and cowboys when they weren't busy working cattle. They usually played cards around the bunk house or on a blanket spread in the shade of the chuck wagon or tree. Cattlemen played poker quite often for big stakes, as the one who won a huge ranch with a hand composed of 4 little sixes. They tell this story about the Cornwell brothers of King City. Warren and Jess were identical twins (difficult to tell apart). They engaged in a poker game with some sheep men in the Pinoche Country of San Benito County, and supposedly lost several thousand dollars. A week later they returned to the gambling scene and Warren took part in a new game. Jess remained outside unnoticed. About 11:30 p.m. when everyone was getting drunk, and several thousand dollars were on the table, Warren excused himself, and notified Jess it was his turn at the cards. Jess staggered in "plumb" sober and within a few hands controlled all the money, thus the Cornwells recuperated their loss together with a handsome profit.

Poker was first introduced in the southern states by two sons of wealthy plantation owners who went to England to school. This game was learned by them and brought back and spread rapidly over the cattle country. The game was first played with about half a deck of cards. Later is was developed and the full deck known today was used. Some of the language that is used today was developed while playing this game of poker. Some of the expressions and phrases are as follows: Bluffer, fourflusher, lay the cards on the table, cash in, show down, ace in the hole, ace high, aces and eights—the dead man's hand, stand pat, calling a bluff, cold deck, sit in, turn down, rotten deal, square deal and even new deal. Poker is a complicated card game; you are on your own — no partner to blame for mistakes!

The long cattle drives and the happenings that went with them probably wrote more history than any other one development of the cattle business. The largest number of cattle driven over these trails was in 1871 when over 600,000 head went north. Today we still have migration of cattle. Each year approximately half a million head go from Texas into the Osage and Flint Hills sections. Between 700,000 and 1 million head are shipped from Arizona, Mexico and Texas into the bur clover and filaree ranges or into feedlots in California.

Even though the cattle business was one of the first industries to be established in our land, it is still flourishing as strong as ever. Its importance will probably continue for some time because 75% of the area called the "West" is composed of rough, untillable rangeland known to the early settler as the free-grass area that can only be harvested by livestock.

We're still here, Longhorns on Arthur Bright's Ranch, Le Grand, Calif.

Our First Cattle

The first cattle to enter the U.S. were basically of the Spanish Longhorn breed, and this was in 1540. This breed of cattle made more colorful history than any other breed known to civilized man. Their history was equal to that of the buffalo.

During the brief period in which he reigned the West from Texas to Canada, the Longhorn steer was the only breed of cattle that could have economically harvested the grass and brush during the free-grass era. This was before the coming of railroads, the invention of barbed wire, and the establishment of windmills to develop water for the great range areas of the West.

Although basically Spanish, the true Longhorn was Texan by origin and birth, the same as was the cowboy who steered him up the long trails north of the "36" through the brush and across rivers and through swamps where they reached market. Finally, they occupied the world that was left empty by the passing of the Indian meat animal known as the American buffalo.

The Longhorn steer had been described as an animal with huge horns. In some cases in the early days, these were as much as 8 feet long from tip to tip. The steers' heads were long and coarse and they had long floppy ears. Their ears were usually marked with many designs showing ownership. They also carried dewlaps, wattles, and jug handles and the brands that they wore more or less resembled relief maps.

They were long-legged and thin of flank with sharp, pointed shoulders and their bodies were so long that sometimes their backs swayed, and they were cat-hammed. But they were not scrubs. Their dressing percentage was said to be quite high, indicating that after all they were not all horns and hide. They matured late, were resistant to disease, and they lived many years. They could walk the roughest ground and swim the widest of rivers. They could cross the most parched desert and climb the highest mountain. They were equipped to fight wolves, coyotes, and many other predatory animals on their range.

They could live on short grass and go miles for a drink and they could run like a race horse on the prairie and were as active as a panther in the brush country. They were truly the cattle of the time and were the only breed that could have existed and harvested the feed of the West at the time they reigned supreme. There is only one other breed that might have equalled but not surpassed them and that is the Brahman.

The Longhorn steer was immune to the Texas fever and he could withstand severe hot weather as well as the blizzards and the cold blasts from the north. It seems to me that today our scientists might use some of the Longhorn blood—although it is getting thin—to improve some of our highly domesticated cattle to be able to withstand hardships particularly cold and heat. A limited amount of research work is being conducted in California comparing the performance of the Longhorn with Hereford cattle. Farm Advisor Don Petersen reports some interesting results are being discovered such as resistance to scours, pinkeye, and production of small calves at birth.

From 1866 to 1890, it was estimated that 10 million head of Texas cattle were driven north to market. It usually cost a dollar a head to deliver these cattle and stories indicate that barrels of money were made by trail drivers, most of whom died broke.

One of the methods used to "improve" the Texas Longhorn was that if a calf looked as if it would not make a good steer, it was kept for a bull. Longhorn cattle were skittish and they would stampede at the drop of a hat, although when they did stampede they stayed bunched together better than any other breed of cattle. It is estimated that on some of the worst stampedes these cattle would travel 10 to 12 miles. They had a keen sense of smell and on occasions have been known to smell water 12 miles away. Very thirsty herds became unmanageable when they smelled water and all one could do was follow them until they had their fill.

Many stories have been told about the Maverick. The story goes that in 1961 a man by the name of Samuel Maverick in Texas owned more land and cattle than anybody else in the U.S. at that time. He was said to be chicken-hearted and did not favor branding and marking his animals. Since everyone else had an iron, he was of the opinion that everything not marked or branded belonged to him, thus the saying, "There goes a Maverick."

Each trail boss usually had a lead steer. It was a bovine that was first off the bed ground, would mill the herd during a stampede, lead the bunch across raging rivers and through unexplored rough terrain. Some of these pace setter steers were even broke to lead. At times when the herd became unmanageable, a cow hand would rope their natural born leader and point the way to get the herd moving again.

One great lead steer was called "Old Blue" because of his blue roan color. This unusual animal's leadership was used for more than one trail drive. When the herd reached its destination or market point, the cowboys would turn "Old Blue" loose and he would follow them back to Texas. However, after completing about four drives, they left him in Montana, so they thought. In about six months Old Blue showed up on his Texas home ranch, ready for another drive north. When a movie was made of the long trail drives, Old Blue was the hero and star of the show.

In the early days, cattlemen, at times, would become involved in disputes over ownership of a Longhorn steer. Gun battles would occasionally take place, in which case, many times, no one would get control of the animal. Such "gun battle" steers are said to have roamed the range for years, impossible to rope or corral. They were often called ghost steers, so the legend goes.

Longhorn cattle are long lived. Arthur Bright of Le Grande, California, has two Longhorn steers between 15 and 20 years of age.

In Spain, their mother country, it is not unusual for these cattle to be regular producers past 15 years of age.

This breed of cattle is being preserved in the U.S. Government herd in the Witchita Mountains Wildlife Refuge, Oklahoma. This is a very worthwhile movement on the part of the government, for surely the Longhorn breed of cattle is as important in history and to the development of the West as any animal that ever lived. Several individuals such as Harry Pon of Seneca, Oregon, and Arthur Bright, are building fine herds of Longhorns. Recently a Longhorn breed association has been formed with headquarters in San Antonio, Texas.

During 1969, I observed large numbers of Longhorn cattle in Spain. In their home country they are larger and possess a more "beefy" conformation than those found in America. The Spaniards prefer Longhorns over many breeds because they are highly fertile and long-lived. Polished crowns of the early Longhorn steer decorate offices and home in many parts of the U.S.

These Longhorn cattle are tough and smart—a combination hard to equal and impossible to beat.

Ironclad signatures. "Hap" Magee, cattleman, Danville, Calif.

Hieroglyphics of the Range

Branding cattle has been a custom in America since the time that Cortez, the Spanish conqueror, invaded this new land. Even before that time history indicates that branding was practiced. A tomb 2,500 years old discovered at Thebes bore an image of a cow being branded by a man. Putting designs on livestock was practiced in England as far back as the eighteenth century.

Legally it is recognized above all other methods of showing and proving ownership.

Brands are usually classified as letters, figures, characters, or a combination of these. For example, A is a letter, 5 a figure, and ⚓ a character; A5 is a combination of these.

All legal brands of California are recorded at the office of the State Bureau of Livestock Identification at Sacramento. This is the same principle used in filing serial numbers of automobile engines, that being to avoid duplication and to insure claim of ownership. There are about 30 thousand brands of all designs and descriptions registered in California.

There is a definite language that pertains to brands. For instance, one speaks of a ranch by its owner's brand, such as the double H (⊦⊦) ranch. The herd of cattle might be known as the JB herd. The cowboy might be riding a double O (◉) horse. Another cowpoke is known as the spur (✧⊂) hand, and that cow in the distance looks like a critter bearing the anchor (⚓) brand.

Brands should be clear, simple, and easily read; complicated designs often make unreadable, blurred brands. Brands that are too tired to stand are called "lazy" such as lazy H (⊥). Brands in an oblique or angular position are know as "tumbling," like the tumbling T (◤). A letter or figure that curves at the ends is spoken of as "running," like this (⚲). When it has wings (⚲) it is called a flying W. Brands "walk," "swing," "drag," and "rock," like the rocking chair (⊾). A straight line usually indicates a bar, but when it becomes long it is usually spoken of as a rail. Brands have different names in different sections of the country. In one place, O-O may be spoken of as O bar O; in another as hobble O.

Rustlers sometimes attempt to change brands. This is usually done with a running iron, which is merely a piece of iron about 6 inches long with a curved end. At times rustlers attempt to change the registered iron by applying their hot iron over a wet sack so that the resulting brand looks as if it had been applied several months before. One of the well known episodes of changing a brand took place in southern Monterey County when the famous H-H brand owned by Miller and Lux was changed to read double box arrow (⊟⊟→). Another clever brand change was cross triangle (�) to 4 bar M (4̶M̲).

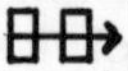

It is unlawful to apply a recorded brand anywhere on the animal except that specified on the registration certificate. Brands denoting ownership are commonly placed on the left or right hip, ribs, or shoulder. Brands are read from top to bottom and from left to right; for example, W̄B̄ is called Bar WB.

Record brands, like numerals, letters, or combinations of numerals and letters to denote the year of birth or age of cattle, can be placed on the right jaw (figure 1) or on either loin in front of the hip and behind the ribs without being registered. Single numbers or a combination may be used in conjunction with and directly below a registered brand. (See figure 2.)

Figure 1. Jaw brand, using the number 2 to show the year of animal's birth (1962).

A cattle record brand for dairy cattle of the Holstein, Jersey, Guernsey, Ayrshire, Brown Swiss, Dutch Belted, and Milking Shorthorn breeds may be placed on the right hip rather than on the loin. Such brand shall be used only for identification and not as evidence of ownership.

When numerals are used for record brands on dairy cattle of these breeds, these numerals must form numbers greater than 200.

When in doubt about the legal aspect of branding cattle, contact your local brand inspector or see the *Agricultural Code of California Pertaining to Marks and Brands.*

A hot iron used to brand cattle should be about the color of white ashes — hot enough to burn the first layer of skin to a light tan within a few seconds. A burn of this kind will heal rapidly, cause scar tissue to form, eliminate hair growth, and make the design visible. Do not permit the iron to slide or the brand may be blotched.

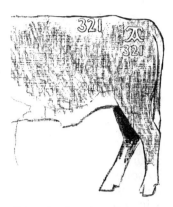

Figure 2. Brand used in combination with numerals. The numeral in the first position designates year of birth (1963). Other numerals designate number of animal (21).

Permanent brands can also be placed on cattle by the proper use of certain chemical preparations. First, clip the area of the animal where the brand is to appear. Then dip the iron into the branding liquid; cover the under surface of the iron to prevent smearing. (See figure 3.)

An owner may use a vent brand to rebrand a branded animal to void the animal's previous brand. A vent brand may be applied on either loin of animal, corresponding to the side of the owner's registered brand. Only the owner's registered brand may be used as a vent.

Figure 3. Chemical brand.

Horn brands are used extensively for identifying cattle. They need not be registered. You can purchase branding irons already made up for this purpose, usually numeral or letter designs. Apply the heated iron on the front of the horn about 1 inch from the base. Don't burn too deeply — about ⅛ inch is enough. (See figure 4.)

Figure 4. Horn brand, using numeral design.

Designs in hair are used to identify cattle for short periods of time. Figure 5 shows an example of a numbering code used by some cattlemen. Designs are usually made with electric clippers and should be the width of the clipper blade and about 4 inches long. It is legal to apply these designs with a hot iron for permanent identification of cattle. When applied in this manner, they must be placed on either loin in front of the hips and behind the ribs, or on the right jaw. They do not have to be registered when placed in these positions.

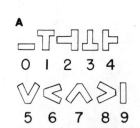

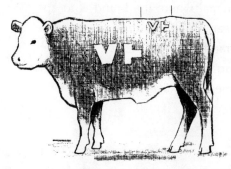

Figure 5. A. Code of hair brands. B. Code 54. (Developed by Kenneth A. Wagnon, Specialist, Department of Animal Husbandry, Davis.)

FREEZE BRANDING

Advantages

—The brand is visible the year round without clipping. Hair comes in white. Pigment is removed from the skin.
—Relatively painless to the animal.

—Does not leave a thick scar like fire branding; such scars reduce hide's value.

—Brands do not blotch.

Disadvantages

—This identification procedure does not legally denote ownership of cattle in California.

—It is time consuming — 30 seconds or more per animal.

—Securing brands by this system is difficult — legibility runs between 50 and 75 percent.

—Since the basis of the brand is the formation of white hair, it's not easy to use on white-haired animals. The freezing destroys the melanocytes (the pigment-producing cells). With no pigment both hair and skin are white. You can use this method on white animals if you overbrand (leave cold iron on animal a longer time — 1 to 1½ minutes) and destroy the hair follicles. There is enough pigment in the skin even in white animals so that it leaves a white brand free of hair.

Follow this procedure:

—Clip the hair from the area to be branded. The closer the clip, the better.

—Dampen the branding area with alcohol for better contact with the iron and to keep it from freezing to the hide.

—The irons are cooled by placing them in a solution of dry ice (solid carbon dioxide) and alcolhol (ethyl, methyl, or isopropyl). Leave the irons in the solution until heavy bubbling or boiling stops. For quantity branding, it pays to have a large enough container to place all of the irons in at once.

—A styrofoam box (12x20x10 inches deep) is satisfactory as an insulated container. Do not use plastic-lined boxes as thin plastic will crack. Dry ice is broken into egg-sized pieces to cover the bottom. Add alcohol (95-percent methyl) to cover the ice by 2 or 3 inches.

—The irons are pressed heavily against the skin for 30 seconds. Copper or bronze round-faced irons with plenty of material have proven to be best (⅝ of an inch wide and at least an inch deep).

—For freeze-branding 100 head of cattle within 3 to 4 hours, 20 pounds of dry ice and 3 gallons of 95-percent alcohol should be ample. You will need to add dry ice to the alcohol from time to time. Under damp atmospheric conditions, change alcohol every 2 hours since it absorbs moisture from the air. This "watered down" alcohol loses its cooling capacity and will begin to slush up as water accumulates and ice forms.

Figure 6. A good freeze brand as seen from a pickup.

Figure 7. Horse brands, showing possible placement on hip, shoulder, jaw, or neck.

Horses can be identified by hot-iron brands placed on the hip, shoulder, or jaw. (See figure 7.) Horse brands should be small. Since the skin of horses is thin and fine, care should be taken not to burn too deeply. Occasionally, horses are numbered on the neck.

Most cattlemen are brand-conscious. They think of brands the year around. It is a common practice of theirs to whittle a brand out while sitting on a rail fence or doodle one while talking on the telephone. They carve their brands on trees, and it was customary in the cow country for the cowman's son to put his father's brand on the school desk. They carved their brands in their spur straps and belts, and many a one has been etched on a six-shooter that helped to win the West.

Even the cooks who followed the chuck wagons sometimes designed the owner's brand in the crust of a delicious apple pie. It is not uncommon to see brands shakily drawn on barroom walls and floors. Of late it is fashionable to invite cattlemen to burn their irons in the walls of popular saloons or bars; thus, decorating the liquor establishment with a Western flavor.

Most cattlemen are very proud of their brands. They will have them stamped on the cantle of their saddles, on the wings of their chaps, on their stationery, check books and pickup truck doors. One cattleman has his brand mounted on the hood of his Cadillac. It is not unusual to have the brand stamped on the front steps of his home.

Combining work with pleasure, branding parties are an important feature of the cowman's social life. Neighbors and friends for miles around gather up the unbranded animals of the host's herd, leave the imprint of the hot iron on each, and at the completion of their chores relax and enjoy a good old-fashioned barbecue, thereby getting a "taste" of the brand!

Cowboys, when out on the range, will sometimes rope deer, coyotes and other wild life and invariably will put their employer's brand on them.

Most people who are engaged in this old and colorful industry take pride in knowing brands. They are as adept at this as a hotel clerk in knowing the names of clientele, a professor in remembering the names of his students, and a bartender at retaining names of whiskeys. But the memory of brands tops all of these because you need to have an instinct for cattle to know brands. Most cattle inspectors know thousands of them. In fact, one old cattle inspector said that he knew what brand the animal was wearing by tasting the meat.

To pick out a brand and name it is a serious, important business with a real cowman, even more important than naming his son. A good brand usually has straight lines and should be easy to read. Sometimes it designates the cattle owner's name. Important incidents which take place in the lives of cow people are often responsible for their individual brand. An illustration of this was the young man from the east who came west because of his tubercular condition, so the story goes. He regained his health and became a large cattle operation. He felt that the high, dry air of the Rockies was responsible for his recuperation and success so his brand was AIR.

My father traded a pair of corduroy pants for his double **HH** brand. The former owner, Bill Woodard was on his way to the gold fields of Alaska, and he reasoned that the pants would be more valuable to him than money.

My brother Ed's ranch is called Frosty Acres, so he chose snowman's face for his brand (**∵**) a fitting trademark.

Another prominent cattleman made his first money in the oil business and thus chose OIL as his trademark. A blacksmith went into the ranching game and took as his brand the anvil (◁▢). But probably one of the most famous stories of how a man chose his iron was that of a young cowpuncher who sat in a poker game in Dodge City many years ago. At first his luck was bad, but as dawn approached he started winning. By sunup he had won all the money in the house. One of the victims who had gone entirely broke suggested that they play one more hand and he would stake his ranch against the cowboy's winnings. The first five cards drawn by the famous gambler were two little 6's and the second drawing he drew two more, the four 6's winning the cattle ranch. He immediately branded his cattle with the four 6's (6666).

It's an art to brand cattle, especially with a running iron, which is merely a piece of iron about six inches long with a curved end. Oldtimers were proud of their writing when it was done on the hide of a critter.

This double **HH** brand was acquired by Henry Miller from a man named Henry Hildreth of Merced County, and probably more cattle bore this stamp than any other in California. The running W (**ᴡ**) is in all probability the only brand that has been run on more critters than the **HH**, this brand being owned by the King Ranch in Texas.

According to legend, all it took to get into the cattle business in the early days was a long rope, a running iron, and plenty of nerve. Most of the people who settled the West in the days when the cattle business was in its glory had all three of these prerequisites. The majority of the cattlemen were honest and their character above reproach.

As long as we have the hills and the mountains and the plains in this country that lies west of the 100th meridian, that portion of the West that mothered the buffalo, the coyote and the prairie dog, branding cattle will be a necessary practice if the grass of that area is to be harvested.

Do You Know Dirt?

The homestead. Albaugh ranch, as it looked in 1884.

Deep down in everyone's heart there is a longing to own a piece of "Mother Earth." This desire is apparently a primitive instinct that civilization has failed to erase in mankind. Since there is a limit on the acreage available, and with population increasing rapidly, most lands, in California especially, are in great demand. There are many yardsticks available to guide either the newcomer or the old-timer in the purchase of a ranch. Regardless of outlines that may be available to guide one in appraising a piece of property, there are a few fundamentals that should be considered.

One of the first considerations would be to determine what type of soil makes up this proposed "dream ranch." Generally speaking, the heavy, deep, well-drained soils are the most productive. As a rule they outyield the light, shallow fields. If you are not trained in soil types there is available a soil map of California in each Extension farm advisor's office that is fairly accurate on this subject. A thorough study of this map together with the narrative that goes with it, can be exceedingly helpful in determining what type of soil a piece of property contains.

Fertility is a very important quality of any soil. It has been shown by the Division of Agronomy at the University of California, that fertility may be as important as moisture for production of early feed. This is true in range areas where the rainfall is near 15 inches.

A second consideration should be the nature of the terrain or topography of the ranch. A rough, rocky, brushy ranch usually is not nearly as productive nor accessible as a gentle, rolling, brush-free area. Livestock, grazing in rough terrain, will not usually gain as rapidly as those on land that is more gentle in slope.

The third item to consider would be the nature of feed produced on the ranch to be purchased. Is there a strong growth of legumes and grasses, such as bur or Spanish clovers coupled with filaree, and some of the better brome grasses, with a sprinkling of good perennials, such as the stipa and melica? If so, it would be a much more productive beef or sheep ranch than one that is contaminated with the weedy, annuals, such as the ripguts and foxtails. To avoid future catastrophies, a search should be made for poisonous plants that may be growing on the ranch, such as larkspur, wild parsnip, lupines, etc.

An appraisal should be made as to whether or not your range feed could be protected from fire hazards. Are there roads available through the ranch so that wild fires can be suppressed easily? Is the surrounding territory one in which there is a large amount of travel by undesirable or negligent people? Isolation from transient tourists is desirable.

Fourth, there is a saying that "water makes the difference between profit and loss." Any ranch should be well-watered. Livestock can live longer without feed than they can without water. Water is important to digestion of food and the health of animals. This was very markedly demonstrated during the great blizzards in Nevada in 1948. Thousands of cattle died that year, trapped on the desert because of insufficient water. They were supplied feed by the hay lift but couldn't digest it because of lack of "Adam's ale." Cattle should not be made to walk more than 2½ miles to water. Sheep can travel a distance of about 4 miles. Watering facilities should be so constructed and available that animals can secure ample, clean, fresh water at all times. In purchasing a ranch the owner should also determine whether or not the water rights are secure. This is very important and has been since the beginning of the cattle business in the west. It might be a good idea to determine what mineral rights go with the property and whether a title for them is adequate.

Fifth, fencing and equipment are important parts of any

livestock operation. Too much fancy equipment only adds extra expense to the ranch and does not pay the necessary dividends. Yet, unless the ranch is properly fenced, it is difficult to carry on a range improvement program, and it is also impossible to develop a selective breeding program for improving the cow herd or the sheep flock.

Sixth, climate should receive a lot of consideration. The prospective owner should determine whether he wants to live in a hot mild, or cold climate, or if he wants a desert or high mountain operation, or in between. Rainfall, in any case, is important. On some of the better ranches the annual rainfall is between 15 and 20 inches per year. Usually if this is distributed over a period of several months it is what we call, in a cow man's language, "a surer feed ranch." Temperature has a great bearing on the weight gains of livestock. If the temperatures are too high, the animal's appetite fails and consequently the gains are reduced. Where the climate is very cold more feed is required to produce a pound of gain than in the milder climate because of the extra feed used to keep the animal warm.

Seventh, access to a good market is an important consideration in purchasing any piece of property. Generally, it costs about one cent a pound more to market an animal from Modoc County than it does from Sacramento County. Unless the animal could be produced that much cheaper in Modoc County, Sacramento County property would be a better buy with everything else being equal.

Eighth, location of the ranch in relation to additional rental property is another consideration that is often overlooked. For example, if the cattle are wintered in one area and summered in another area these two pieces of property should be as close together as possible. Trailing or trucking cattle long distances to feed is expensive.

Ninth, wherever available, study production records on the ranch that you are interested in buying. Such records may be secured from the ranch owner, from banks or other credit houses, and occasionally such information can be secured from county farm advisors. Ordinarily, a ranch in California should produce between 15 and 20 pound of beef per acre per year. Irrigated pasture ranches, if properly managed, will produce about 500 pounds of beef per acre per year. These are only averages and are a base from which to start analyzing production records. Production of any ranch is more or less dependent upon management of it.

Tenth, the livestock disease problem is another important item to investigate in purchasing a ranch. Will you have to vaccinate for anthrax and "red water?" Is it in an area where a high percentage of the livestock have aborted? Is is surrounded by contaminated streams? These are some of the items that will have to be decided upon before you can make an intelligent purchase.

Eleventh, is this piece of property that you are about to spend your life's savings on suitable for diversification? Will you have to put all your eggs in one basket and run only one type of livestock or can you grow and produce two or three types of animals profitably? Is it possible to grow some other cash crops in addition to livestock? As one old cowman said, "The reason that I have been a success is because I have had something to sell every day." He had a diversified ranch.

Twelfth, what are the possibilities of improving production through improved management? Can additional water be developed on this ranch to which you are about to seek title? Can improved varieties of range grasses and legumes be successfully grown on it? Will the proper fertilization add income and swell your bank account? Can high quality, young desirable cattle be successfully produced on this ranch? Can a high percent of calf crop be secured that is produced early in the year and from a short calving season? Will the cattle on this particular ranch be heavy for their age? That is, will weaner calves weigh between 450 to 600 pounds?

The late Professor H. R. Guilbert perfected a rule-of-thumb that could be quite effectively used when purchasing a ranch. He stated that when cattle were worth 30 cents a pound and you wanted to earn 5 percent interest in your investment, you could afford to pay $470 per animal unit for land and facilities. He further stated that in California it took approximately 285 pounds of beef per animal unit to pay for the cost of running or carrying an animal unit per year.

After you have "chewed over" a few of these suggestions and have acquired title to this livestock ranch, then it might be a good idea to take stock in your own ability to run it. Do you have the fundamental and scientific knowledge on feeding and breeding livestock? Can you put into practice efficient sound production methods? Do you have the knowledge and "know how" of marketing livestock? This is especially important on a "sticky" buyers market. On the other hand, do you have that natural gift of knowing and sensing a good buy when you see it? These qualities are based on inheritance and early training; they are difficult to acquire. Henry Miller, the great western cattle baron had them and he acquired a million acres of land and a million head of cattle during the roaring 80's and the gay 90's. Old timers used to say, "Henry knew dirt."

This is Country

Are you one of those red-corpuscled westerners who yearn to feel the magnetic tingle of this land of the setting sun? Wouldn't you relish again getting off the trodden paths to the still whispering land? That land where the hand of man not yet has marred that royal handicraft of Mother Nature; where the leafy roads are still those our pioneer fathers brushed out as they trekked silently through this great vastness; where cool lakes, sassy streams, green primeval forests and nature's wildlife not yet have gone commercial under the tramping feet of advancing civilization?

Would you truly like to rough it and once more breathe the uncontaminated mountain air laden with invigorating oxygen? What a thrill it would be to put your feet again on virgin soil and let the mountain sunrays wash your skin of that urban masque and heap it full of vitamin D. If you have a longing and a desire to see nature "a la natural" then spend a week or so in exploring and deep drinking in of those scenic wonders of the Siskiyous and the Sierras of northern California.

This untrampled tract fully possesses about all that is left unspoiled of the "Great West" and typical of its rugged traditions and wild splendor is Bill Lunsford of McArthur, Shasta County, hunter, guide, and mountainman of that country.

Just a word concerning Bill, for like the country he will guide you through, he grips you, not only by his ready Irish wit and open friendliness, but also by his profound knowledge and familiarity of those parts where the fighting redskin made his last grand stand. Bill is a descendant of that hardy and courageous pioneer stock known to all the West as "trail blazers." His father came west to Modoc County in 1868 and was an interpreter between the Indians and whites during the whole of the bloody Modoc wars. Needless to say Bill acquired a deep love for this wild country that has always been his home. With his keen student's mind he has stored up copious knowledge of the far famed lava beds of the Modoc and its surrounding country, a first-hand practical knowledge that is unsurpassed today.

"Glass Mountain," one of the first wonder spots Bill will

take you to see, is by far the most fascinating and gripping portion of this part of California. It is a gigantic mountain of about 80 miles around at the base, the largest obsidian formation in the world. Its glass flow — a mass of jet black substance resembling molasses which glistens and sparkles in the sun — is 300 feet high, 1420 feet wide, and 1¼ miles long, is not only a unique sight but awe inspiring. This huge mountain harbors a full 7 miles of pure lava flow, mute evidence indeed, even to the scientist, of the immense heat and pressures that ages ago visited this crucible country.

Bill will point out to you on this unusual "hill" ice caves where the temperature today is like that of the Arctic Circle, while but a few steps away hot smoky steam jetties are spouting forth. A cinder cone butte magnificently made up of queer spongy pumice formation adds greatly to the wonder of Glass Mountain. Then, too, one of the last and by far the best stands of yellow and sugar pine timber found anywhere in America is located on this mountain. This excellent stand of pine is 18 miles long and 3 miles wide and has never known the touch of axe or saw. In addition to these weird and truly unusual wonders that have all been heaped and stirred together on one mountain, the Builder of Builders saw fit to place a beautiful deep-blue, sub-alpine, snow-watered lake on its very summit. Centuries ago Indians named this body of pure water "Medicine Lake" because of its medicinal properties. This lake was used as a retreat and healing place for Indian warriors of many tribes. It is 1½ miles long, ¾ of a mile wide and is said to be 600 feet deep. This is really a spot par excellence to camp, fish, hunt, and swim; all of this and ideally located in the heart of the wonders of "Glass Mountain."

Upon leaving Glass Mountain and traveling north some 30 miles you will encounter the traditional and historical part of Modoc County; namely, "Captain Jack's Stronghold." This battleground of one of the bloodiest Indian wars ever fought contains about 1,500 acres of exceptionally rough lava conntry. Here on this rugged land where no poppy ever raised its golden head, from December 6, 1872 until May 1873, 60 fighting Modoc braves led by the brainy and crafty Captain Jack held a whole army of whites at bay, killing 400 of them without losing a single man. This is probably the most natural battleground God ever built.

One could spend days inspecting this Indian war field, picking up relics, viewing the original forts, caves, and council grounds. It would take modern warfare to rout the enemy from this concealed natural battleground. This fact is brought closer home when one learns that the Modoc war was fought entirely with guns. Bullets did not end this war, they served only as a medium for holding off the whites. It was the lack of a food supply alone that caused Captain Jack and his faithful Indian band to surrender.

The story is told that Captain Jack never did turn his sword over to the whites. Instead, he completely concealed and camouflaged himself with sagebrush stuck through his clothing and escaped from his beseiged stronghold. Three days later in Steel Swamp, some 30 miles to the east, he was captured and later hanged; so ended the last Indian war in America.

On three sides of this famous battlefield there are great stretches of lava country extending as far as the eye can see. It is estimated that there are some 200,000 acres in the grotesque expanse, much of which is said to be yet unexplored. Out in this huge vastness where the silence to uninitiated often becomes thunderous, Old Bill Lunsford, the lava guide, has explored personally and alone over 250 deep caves and caverns.

It is impossible to say which of these caves is the most outstanding, and it is sheer folly for an inexperienced writer to attempt to describe them. Yet a word or two should be said about them.

Fern Cave is very appealing, intriguing, and affords plenty of food for study. From every indication, this underground house was used as winter quarters by the Indians. It amazes the visitor by the queer hieroglyphics found on its ancient walls. Many claim that these writings tell a story of the lava country in the days before the Indians inhabited those parts and that it was the hand of the yellow Chinese that scribbled on its rocky walls and not the flint of the redskin.

Bear Paw Cave, another interesting place, contains the largest ice falls in the world. Apparently a river flowed through this cave while the rocks were still warm and as they gradually cooled, the water became frozen into a beautiful body of clear ice. These falls are said to be some of the oldest frozen water on the globe.

Skull Cave and Frozen River Cave are two hollows of historical nature. The former is so named because of the skulls and carcasses found on its floor; the latter receiving its name from the sleek icy floor indicating that a good size body of water once flowed through its chambers.

The Lunsford Cave was discovered by our guide in 1908 while hunting mule deer. This unusual cavern supports a cooled creek of molten lava. The foam, eddies, and waves of that once hot, molten liquid, remain as natural in this cave as when it floor ran like water.

Caldwell Cave resembles a theatre much more picturesque and colorful than could ever be duplicated by either artist or architect. Mammoth Cave is still to be completely explored but is said to be 2 days long by foot travel.

Besides these interesting caves and others too numerous to expound upon, one finds in this rugged country the largest dry crater in the world, being 750 feet deep and 1,000 feet across. Adjoining this crater is another large depression called the "Devil's Mush Pot" formed by the land sinking, rather than being blown out from within, as is the case in the formation of a crater.

To the north of these far flung lava beds is the great Tule Lake country. This huge agricultural district contains more than 100,000 acres of exceptionally rich land, producing potatoes, barley, oats, alfalfa, and livestock. In the early days, this area was covered with water whose bosom was studded with tules and white pelicans, but man drained off the water and homesteaders moved in to till its virgin soil.

Mr. Webster did not coin words that can justly describe this wild and grotesquely distorted section of the world. All I hope to do is to help whet your interest and curiosity; to create a desire in the hearts of you hardy westerners to visit this unspoiled land, where one can see its uniqueness, beauty, wildness, and color; feel its vastness, its charm, its soil, rocks, and ice, and by all means hear Bill Lunsford tell of its history, its formation, and of the traditional events that have been written by the hand of time across its rugged, wrinkled face.

An early rock fence.

How the Sierra Calls

Winter beauty — Burney Falls.
Courtesy of Willis Albaugh, Shasta Co., Calif.

As the winter days lengthen into the happy spring, and springtime fades into balmy summer, the vacation seeker's traveling eye roams the maps for a quiet, cool, peaceful place to spend a restful vacation.

The vacationist, like the birds, loves the south in winter, but, in summer, the north is the land of his dreams. How far to the northland must one journey before he can find an unique playground, where fishing, hunting and scenery prevail? Where can one find the place where beauty, combined with nature's great network of living, wildlife, trees and flowers will soothe the ragged-edged nerves and serve as an antidote for the long months of confinement in the noisy crowded cities and busy farms? These are a few of the questions that the people interested in recreation are asking.

To these nature and outdoor loving people, northern California offers an excellent opportunity. There the snowy Sierra Nevada's sparkle in the morning sun; old silvery Mt. Shasta, is king, and Mt. Lassen is queen. There the cold clear waters of the McCloud, Fall River, and Hat Creek splash and dash their way to the sea. There the mountain and rainbow trout and black bass have their homes and the black bear browses in the "sarvis" berries. There the deer bed down in the snow brush, and the antelope roam the plains. That is the land of real northern California, and a section that offers ace-high recreation to the tourist who likes it rough and wild.

It matters little which place the mountain lover chooses, for he will find all the pleasures of outdoor life there to greet him. The cool nights are not too cool for enjoyable camping. Let's journey to the Lassen National Park which is just being developed. Here we find three beautiful clear lakes in which to fish and swim, and if we like to row, these waters are splendid for that also. Some of the best varieties of trout are found in these lakes, and Butte Lake, which lies just next door to the park, is especially noted for its large fish.

Fishing is not the only feature of this picturesque country, for we have nature's clever art work to look upon. Traveling down Hat Creek, which is alive with mountain trout, we see the famous devastated area, which was formed in 1915 when the big mud flow descended from Mt. Lassen after she had belching hysteria. Then, too, we have the one and only Devil's Kitchen, and Cinder Cone to explore, as well as the pleasure of ascending and peering into the crater of the only active volcano in the United States. These scenic spots are unique for no other like them can be found elsewhere in the world. After one has rested his wandering eye on these places, one has an added view of life, as well as new food for thought concerning just how this old world was made.

Farther down Hat Creek, we drop down into one of the prettiest valleys, for its size, in the world. It carries the creek's name. By advantageously using the waters of this mountain creek, the farmers of this valley produce enormous crops of alfalfa, which are fed to their dairy and beef cattle. On some of the richer lands, seed potatoes are grown to supply many other sections of the state. Seed potatoes that grow in this rich northland possess much vigor and vitality and, when later planted in the southern part of the state, grow well and produce bumper crops.

Upon leaving Hat Creek Valley, and before reaching Fall River Valley, one passes by one of the prettiest scenes in America, Burney Falls. These falls are formed by the waters of Burney Creek dropping over a rocky cliff a distance of approximately 96 feet. The falls get their name from a pioneer, who blazed his way into the mountain country during the early fifties. The legend is that Burney fell in love with an Indian maiden and upon the day he was to marry her, the chief of her tribe ordered Burney to be put to death by going over the falls in a canoe. Burney Falls was purchased by Frank McArthur in 1920 and deeded to the state of California for a park, in memory of his late father and mother. Thanks to God for giving us big-hearted, nature-protecting men like McArthur, for had he not deeded this beauty spot to the state, some power company would have harnessed Burney Creek's water, thus destroying its beauty forever, as with the famous Pit River Falls.

From this wonder spot, we wind our way up one of the most noted rivers in California, known as the Pit. Digger Indians who inhabited this country in the early days dug pits along the banks of the stream for the purpose of trapping wild game, thus the name. This river is the home of some of the largest and greatest hydro-electric power plants in the world. Here one can see how man bridles the snowy mountain waters that generate electricity, to supply the needs of other sections of the state.

Some twenty miles pursuing the source of Pit River, we pass through a number of mountain valleys, namely Cayton, Fall River, Big Valley and Hot Spring. These valleys all resemble one another, in that they all have fertile soil and ample water for irrigation. The farmers of these garden spots have taken advantage of the two natural resources and produce excellent crops of alfalfa, cereals, fruits, and truck gardens.

Upon leaving the Pit River Valley country, one can journey northwest to the scenic wilds of the McCloud River territory. Here trout fishing is again at hand, together with some of the best forest and mountain views of the state. At last, we arrive at Mt. Shasta, the monarch of his tribe. If our desires are such, and our physique strong enough, we can, ascend her lofty, snowy crown. From here, one can either go north into Shasta Valley and across the state line into Oregon, or turn homeward by the Sacramento canyon route.

For the man or woman who is willing to sacrifice a few good roads in order to see wonderful mountains, lakes, streams, forests, wild life and valleys of rich agricultural land, northern California, among the Sierras, should be considered before deciding upon a trip this summer.

Dad's cronies, left to right: George Corder, Boler Rucker, W. J. Albaugh, Ceryl Schott and Ned Bognuda.

Bells of Eldorado

Eldorado has a rich Spanish sound which is fitting and appropriate to California. This golden county, the champion of the Mother Lode Country, teems with history, tradition and color. It was on the banks of the sandy, rushing American River that John Sutter's man, John Marshall, picked up pebbles of gold, a discovery that stampeded people from all walks of life to that state that lies on the shores of the blue Pacific.

Miners with their picks, pans and shovels put California on the map. Many of these immigrants, eager and restless in search of the yellow dirt, found on arriving in California that there were other types of gold besides that found by Marshall. Among these were grass and cattle for which some of the miners gave up mucking.

In this area, which includes Eldorado, Amador and other counties, some cattle ranches have been in operation for more that 100 years. The Bacchi Ranch is one of these. A visit to this ranch recently gave the writer the pleasure of meeting Francis Bacchi, who is now ramrodding the outfit that his grandfather started years ago.

His ranch is typical of many in that area, and it was a pleasure to find this wide-awake beef producer up-to-date on many of the new methods connected with managing cattle ranches and improving range conditions.

The Bacchis run several hundred head of good quality white-faced cows, pasturing them in the foothills in the winter and trailing them to the high mountains for summer grazing in the area known as the Georgetown, Ice House, and Rubicon River districts. This high range is located approximately 35 to 40 miles from the home ranch.

The drive to the mountain range is probably the last of what might be called the "long trail drives" in California. This summer range produces excellent feed but is very rough and rugged.

One of the practices followed by the cowmen in that area which is unusual to most areas of the West is the use of large numbers of cow bells on their animals. It is interesting to note that every animal, from yearlings up to the old cows, is decorated every spring with a bell.

The Bacchis buy these bells by the dozens. They are all shapes, sizes and tunes. This belling system reduces labor costs in gathering cattle and in keeping hunters from shooting animals on the open range. It also cuts down losses caused by animals straying to other ranges.

The bells are removed from the animals in the winter time. During the slack period the bells are repaired, new clappers are installed and bell straps are mended. Leather to make the straps is purchased by the hide. It is interesting to see the systematic way in which these cowmen go about this practice of belling their cows in the spring. Belling time becomes one of the big occasions on most of these ranches. Some cows get the same bell each year.

Cowboys become experts on cow bell "music" and can tell what cow it is in the brush from the tune of the bell a quarter of a mile away.

Francis Bacchi can display some bells with bullet holes in them, the result of some so-called hunter practicing his marksmanship on one of Eldorado's bells. There is no question that this practice of belling cattle in steep, inaccessible country is a labor-saving device that pays big dividends. But it happens to go a little deeper than that.

Most cowmen get a great thrill out of hearing the musical tune of a bell worn by a whitefaced cow while grazing on the grassy, shady banks of a mountain stream in an alpine mountain valley deep in a yellow pine forest. This is sweet music to their ears. This is especially true if it is coupled with the sound of a bawling bull in the early morning pursuing his challenger or a lone cry of a coyote calling his mate at dusk on a summer evening.

The sound of bells is one of the pleasures and thrills real cattle people get out of their business—one of the many benefits that cannot be measured in dollars and cents. The sound of a cowbell in the woods and mountains can be a powerful lift to a tired cowboy riding the outskirts of the open range.

"Bobwire"

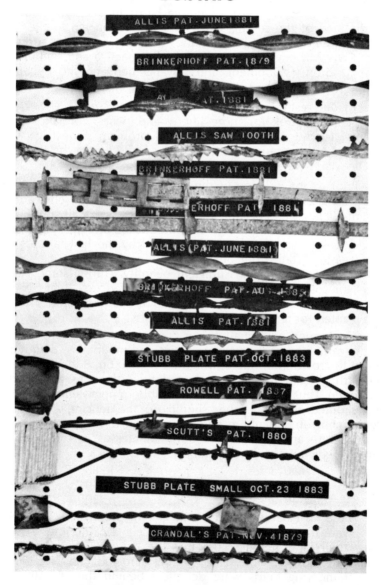

They fenced the west — barbed wire — unusual varieties.

Barbed wire—hated, cursed and pronounced by cowboy and plainsman alike "bobwire"—was a necessary child of our early, colorful West. Without it the vast regions of plains, mountains and deserts lying between the 100th Meridian westward to the Pacific Ocean would never have been entirely tamed and settled. "Bobwire" with its sharp, defensive barbs has meant as much to the land of the setting sun as has the cotton gin to the old South. Both were products of the industrial revolution of the post-Civil War era and each played its respective and significant role in the development and advancement of the sections represented.

As our restless and eager forefathers pressed westward in their fanatical trek for more liberty and riches, for lands and bounty, fencing inevitably was a vital problem. Especially was that true upon entering the great plains region from the Rockies to Ole Man River, the Mississippi.

Prior to the invasion of the true West, timber was plentiful along the eastern seaboard and backdoor states, and enclosures of farming lands and pasture areas were made with rails split from logs and laid about eight high and interlocked at angles of about 60 degrees. Stones for fences were used by the first farmers in some eastern states, but out West neither timber nor rock materials were to be had in sufficient quantity. During some early years, the osage orange tree was used for fencing. It has been estimated that in 1860, over 60,00 miles of this thick, stout hedge was planted for fence in our prairie country.

The farmer, or "squatters" or "nesters" as they were called by the cattlemen of the western plains and mountains, definitely began to crowd in on the cowman from 1870 on. Both stockmen and struggling homesteaders wanted their domains and fields kept open. Thus, each with the same stubborn persistency thought and shouted that the other should do the fencing. The U.S. Department of Agriculture here saw reason to enter the "fence war" picture and in 1871 put out estimates as to the cost of fencing, which were about as follows:

640 acres	$1,280
160 acres	640
40 acres	320

These cost data, together with gleeful propaganda of their own, were used by the "nesters" to force the cattle interests to fence their lands under claim that the larger the acreage the smaller the cost per acre. Thus, the big barons of the West with their thundering herds were definitely behind the "8-ball" so they took to barbed wire and strung it throughout the new land.

The Department of Agriculture, the same year, 1871, also estimated that there was $198,816,182 invested in fences in the U.S. This survey was made before the famed barbed wire was invented and well in advance of the time when the spectacular and romantic West was wired together with the bobwire.

In 1867, a practical man in Ohio by the name of Lucern B. Smith patented the first defensive armor for a wire fence. It consisted of stout wooden pegs strung on the wire at intervals. Later in 1868, William D. Hunt and Michael Kelly, both from New York, invented other types of armed fence wire which embodied the basic ideas for the later barbed wire construction.

Six years later J. F. Glidden, a farmer of De Kalb, Illinois, patented the most practical and popular barbed wire ever to be designed. Most authorities did agree that although Smith, Hunt, and Kelly had the first basic ideas on armed fences, Glidden was the first to make such ideas practical; therefore, today he is known and recognized as the father of the present gigantic barbed wire industry.

It is said that the idea of a barbed wire came to Glidden while he was fencing a flower garden for his wife. He immediately went into action and deftly placed short pieces of jagged point wire on a single smooth wire. This unheard of type of wire fencing proved highly practical in keeping the dogs and roving cows, as well as neighbors, off the flower beds. It later was equally valuable in helping to conquer the West and wire it down so that the virgin soils could be cultivated and their crops go unmolested.

Following closely on Glidden's heels in this fencing innovation was a man named Jacob Haish. Haish patented the famous "S" barbed feature in the wire, which was as practically efficient as Glidden's and was a close rival for years.

Thus far in the embryo stages of a new industry, barbed wire fencing was strictly a middle-western product, sold only to plains settlers and western customers and practically unknown in the eastern states. Finally in 1876 an eastern concern known as Washburn and Moen Manufacturing Company became interested in this new and revolutionary type of fence. After being unable to purchase Mr. Haish's patents, Charles F. Washburn of this concern then turned to Glidden and was successful in purchasing part of his interests and the right to manufacture for a mere $60,000. Through this deal, Washburn and Moen Manufacturing Company was able to control all of Glidden's patents and thereby the basic patents of Smith, Hunt and Kelly. In this way a practical monopoly of the barbed wire business of the U.S. was established. (These manufacturers were also granted patents in England and

Europe, all of this as early as 1876-77.)

The first barbed wire was made by hand. A Mr. Putnam invented a machine in 1875 which manufactured about 5 ton per day. The first wire sold for 18c per pound or 20c per rod from such early processes. The price today for good common 14½ gauge wire is 18c per rod.

Barbed wire has long been described by galled and harassed stockmen as something primitive, suggestive of savagery, and totally lacking in refinement, but after all harmonizing well with the hardness and toughness of the West. When it was first produced and exhibited as an advertisement of painted posts, one old westerner thought it a "plumb" modern fence, the barbs being the posts; another thought it purely a "new fangled bit" for a horse.

The coming of bobwire marked the first major factor in the decline of the cattle barons of the early West. Its birth recorded and hastened the passing of the open range, free from Texas to Montana; the famed Longhorn steers became fewer and fewer; the noted mustang horses dwindled into small occasional bands.

"Bobwire" soon made possible the introduction and use of purebred stock with control of herds and necessary segregation, though the savage wire wrote "finish" to the long trail drives and turned the cattle trails to the north into measley crooked lanes. With its help, intensive and rotation farming became more and more important in many parts of the West, even replacing livestock ranching. The introduction of bobwire made it easy for settlers to fence and control valuable water holes and desirable lands, to much of which they had no right or title. Being unaccustomed to fences, large herds were often injured. With open, torn flesh they were immediately victims of the vicious screwworm of the southwest, which took unbelievable toll.

Later, wire cutters rode across the scene and many miles of the new hated fences were cut to loose-end ribbons. In spite of all these disadvantages and antagonisms, barbed wire sales increased, miles of fences sprang into existence and the wire was soon common throughout all the cattle country.

In 1874 only 10,000 pounds were manufactured. A year later 600,000 pounds were marketed. At the turn of this century 297,-338,000 pounds were sold, while in 1936, 350,000,000 pounds were used by farmers and stockmen of this country in keeping their stock "in bounds." This last figure is enough wire to build a three-strand fence 375,000 miles long. According to a report of the American Iron and Steel Company, in 1936 farmers of the U.S. used more than 3 billion pounds of wire of one form or another, most of which was in fencing of various types.

Arthur G. Warren, secretary of the American Steel and Wire Company, once stated that now there were over 240 different styles of barbed wire. The famous flat ¼-inch twisted ribbon wire with knife-like barbs welded on at 6-inch intervals; the saw-tooth wire where the barbs are on one edge like a saw; the linked barbed wire with barbs placed in the center of six-inch links; the "S" barbs wound around two ordinary line wires; the dia-mond-shaped barbs strung on one single wire, and the many different types of plain barbed wire, varying in size of line wires, length of barbs, etc., makes a huge list of wire fencing that was said by the old-time cattlemen to have spoiled the raw and early west.

Production of barbed wire by modern methods is highly efficient. The wire is made by twisting two wires known as line wires together and barbs are wound around one or both of these strands. The barbs are placed from 3 to 6 inches apart and have either two or four points. The wire used for the barbs may be round, half-round or flat; but, in all cases now the barbs are cut off diagonally to make a sharp restrictive point, extending out ⅜ of an inch or more from the line wires. Barbed wire is usually put up on 80-rod reels (1,320 or ¼ mile). The weight varies with the size or gauge of wire and length of barbs. Yes, our livestock of today respect the barbs and meekly stay on "home pastures" out of forbidden fields.

During World War I and II, barbed wire was used to protect trenches, patrol lanes and other areas from sudden attack. War wire differed from domestic wire in that barbs were much longer and strung on a square line instead of along two line wires. Barbed wire fences were once used for telephone lines and aided much in speeding up communication during the pioneer era.

Today one strand of barbed wire charged with electricity is being used extensively with good success for temporary fences. This is an economical type of fence and will turn all types of livestock except sheep.

Time flies, and all things change. And so it is with the spectacular and romantic West which began with the white man's first knowledge of the virgin country and ended near the close of the nineteenth century when the great colorful cattle kingdoms gave way to barbed wire and the plow.

The last chapter of the "Old West" is rich in cattle, the "bent-legged" cowboy, his cow pony and reata, the red-skinned Indian, Chisholm days, famous long cattle drives, and the smoking six gun, but only the old-time cattlemen know and lament the real drama that "bobwire" played in the cavalcade of the West.

Teamed for action — John Weber, Alturas, Calif.

My Kingdom for a Horse

"The outside of a horse is good for the inside of a man" is the saying packed with meaning. For, even today, in this age of mechanization when horses are no longer indispensable to all daily activities, man's equine partner is still able to capture his deep personal interest and admiration.

In many walks of life, the horse is still closely associated with man. But regardless of the extent of the association people would do well to learn more about their equine friends in order that selection of the "right" horse for each individual can be accomplished.

In selecting a light riding horse, many factors must be considered if one is to own an animal that will bring him pride, joy, and pleasure. Before making a final choice, he might well investigate some of its background—who bred the horse, who trained it, and how reliable is its present owner?

Temperament or disposition is important in any riding horse. Some authorities believe this character is inherited, while others are of the opinion that it is acquired. Regardless of the cause of good or bad temperament, only the even, mild-dispositioned animals should be selected.

Age of a horse is also significant. The most useful period of a horse's life is between the ages of 5 and 8 years. A colt at birth usually has a few milk teeth and by 7 months all of the milk teeth have developed. By the time he is 3 years old, the two middle incisors in the upper and lower jaw have emerged. At 4, the intermediate two incisors appear; and 5 all of the permanent incisors are in place and the horse is said to have a full mouth. In geldings and stallions the so-called bridle or wolf teeth occur in both the lower and upper jaw. These small teeth, sometimes found in mares, appear directly back of the corner incisor. On the grinding surface of each incisor there appears a slight colored indentation knows as a cup. As the horse grows older, these cups are worn off. The middle incisors of the lower jaw lose them at 6 years of age. At seven years, the second incisors are worn smooth, and at 8 years, the outside pair of teeth have lost their cups. At 9 years of age, the cups in the middle incisors in the upper jaw disappear. Likewise, at 10 years, the second incisors lose these indentations, and at 11, the entire mouth is smooth of cups. In the young horse, the front and lower teeth meet almost at right angles. As the horse, gets older, this angle becomes more acute and the teeth become longer. Always inspect the mouth of a horse for defective teeth and for overshot or undershot jaws.

There is no such thing as a best breed. Top horses are found in all breeds. Usually horses that are well-bred are more valuable than those with no particular breeding; but, a horse whose sire is a purebred and whose mother is a high-grade animal is likely to be intelligent and useful, with a desirable conformation. This is not always the case, but breeding of horses is just as important as in other lines of livestock.

Training and manners of the horse should also receive the buyer's consideration. Like other animals, the horse remembers early training, and habits developed early in life are difficult to correct. Try to pick a horse whose trainer has a good reputation. His horses are likely to have the proper manner and habits.

The horse should be sound in all respects. Look for ringbone, a bony growth that appears between the ankle and top of the hoof or coronary band. This blemish can be found on either the hind or front feet and may cause lameness that is difficult to correct. Sidebones are similar to ringbone except that the growth does not go entirely around the foot. They, too, may cause lameness and occur on either the inside or outside of both the front and hind feet. The splint is found below the knee on the inside of the cannon bone. Unless it is close to the knee joint, this blemish is not very serious. In this position it may cause lameness. Occasionally, splints may be located on the hind leg, but this is unusual.

The hock on a rear leg is a very important joint. In this area one might find several blemishes that will result in unsoundness. Bone spavin occurs on the inside of the hind leg, bog spavin in the hock joint. A curb appears on the cannon bone of the back leg just below the hock. Poll evil, caused from bruising the head, is found directly back of the ears on top of the poll. This area is often inflamed, and one may find running sores discharging pus. A fistula is located on top or directly in front of the withers. It too may be a running sore discharging pus. Occasionally, a horse gets the point of his hip knocked down, and is known as a hipshot horse. This condition does not injure the horse materially, but does impair its looks. Other known blemishes are wind puffs, capped hocks, and cocked ankles. If you are unfamiliar with these unsoundnesses and blemishes, have someone inspect the horse before you purchase him.

Inspection for right conformation should start first on the feet and legs and then continue over the rest of the body. There is an old saying, "No feet, no horse." The feet should be in proportion to the horse's size. Small feet on large horses are not desirable or vice versa. The feet should be wide and deep at the heel. Narrow heels are usually an indication of unhealthy feet, while feet that are shallow at the heel are known as flat feet. Flat-footed horses are not surefooted.

The pastern, which is the bone from the ankle to the top of the hoof, should be moderately long with plenty of slope, yet strong. Horses with short, straight pasterns are often rough riding and generally become unsound. The cannon bone, between the ankle and knee, should be short, flat and clean. A short cannon bone indicates that a horse has good action. The forearm, that part of the leg from the shoulder to the knee, should be heavily muscled both inside and out. The same is true for the part of the hind quarter known as the gaskin. The more slope the shoulder has the better. This makes for easy riding. Generally speaking, horses with this type of conformation will have prominent withers and a short back.

The head size of the horse should be in proportion to the rest of the body. Eyes should be large, prominent and kind. There should be plenty of width between the eyes and the distance from eyes to nostrils must not be too long. Large nostrils are considered desirable. A moderately slender neck that blends in well with the shoulders is sought. The back must be short, and the rump level and long. Straight hind legs, not sickle-hocked, accompany good conformation. The bottom line of the horse should be long and level, with plenty of depth in the flank. The action of the horse ought to be smooth and straight, snappy and yet not too high. Horses that toe-in or paddle do not have proper action.

Bad habits occur in horses the same as in men. Among some of these are stall pulling. This can often be detected by the type of halter and rope used. If it is a heavier and stronger than usual, expect this habit. Horses that have straps buckled tightly around their throat latch are called cribbers. Energy-consuming habits are stall trotting and weaving. Where the stall of the horse is marked with footprints and where the hind legs are skinned and injured, the animal may be a kicker. Some horses are herdbound or balky. It is difficult to ride such horses away from others. Head throwing is often associated with poor training. Such a horse has either been put into the bridle too soon or the hands of the trainer were too heavy. The result of this is usually a poor mouth. Switch-tail horses fall in this same class.

It is often difficult to detect blindness in horses. The eyes can be tested by making a fast motion in front of the horse with your hand or by leading him over some object in an area unknown to him. A windbroken horse can be tested by running him a short distance to test his wind for a roaring sound.

Horses that shy at objects may have poor eyesight or may have acquired this as a bad habit.

Selecting horses is not an easy task. It requires a full knowledge of the anatomy of a horse and all of its functions. It takes "know how," coupled with experience in riding and handling horses, to do the job well.

Thoroughbred Polo Ponies.

Courtesy Lester Sterling

Horses Are Indispensable

Well mounted — Shorty Williamson, King City, Calif.

From time immemorial man has been closely associated with, and exceedingly interested in, horses. Skeletons of the prehistoric horse and that of man indicate that they were partners as early as the stone implement age, or about 4500 years ago. Scientists agree that man first hunted horses for food, then drove them, and later rode them as beasts of burden. Fossil records of the evolution of the horse are more complete than they are for any other animal. The tiny eohippus horse, only 11 inches high with four toes on each front foot and three on each hindfoot, lived about 60 million years ago.

The horse's beauty, intelligence and value to man in civilizing and improving the world are some of the main reasons that this equine animal has fully captured and completely held human interest. A great horse lover once said, "Show me a man that loves a horse, and I'll show you a man of which there's nothing wrong." This is a stout statement but here in California where horses play such an exceedingly important part in developing ranches and recreational programs, the phrase is mighty fitting. "The outside of the horse is good for the inside of man" is another statement packed full of meaning.

The horse has been the companion and servant of man in nearly all of his migrations and conquests. Without the horse the development of our modern world would have been exceedingly difficult.

Books and literature galore have been published about man's most noble servant. Over 2,000 are said to have been printed in England, and an equal number elsewhere. In our own Library of Congress in Washington, D.C., over 1,000 volumes have been assembled, while other departments of our government have specialized more on the subject.

History of our country would indeed lose much of its color and romance if the deeds of our great horsemen were eliminated. Browse around the Capitol at Washington and there you will see many of history's great warriors perpetuated in marble and bronze, mounted upon great chargers that had carried them to victory. To discontinue this practice would be breaking a custom of over 1,000 years.

The prehistoric horse had disappeared from North America before Columbus discovered it. Cortez, a Spanish conquistador, is given credit for bringing the first horses to this continent. De Soto also brought horses with him, which are said to have been abandoned in the country that is now the state of Texas. These early horses were of the Arab and Barb breeds. They multiplied rapidly in the plains country and resulted in what was known in the early days as the Spanish mustang or the western cow pony.

Those early-day cow horses as illustrated by the great western cowboy artist, Charles Russell, resemble in conformation our present-day, popular Quarter Horse. They would pass for Three Bars' colts. To document this statement pages 38, 58, 76, 116 and 156 of the CHARLES RUSSELL BOOK for paintings of cow horses that were popular on the Montana range in the 1880's. In addition to being a top painter, Russell was a recorder of history, and he made few mistakes on the canvas. The horses in his paintings were not muscle-bound, mutton withered, short-legged, and showed no steep pasterns. They were the kind of animals that would bring you home from a long ride without spur or ramol.

After a time, draft breeds were imported in the country and crossed with the mustang. The Clydesdale, Percheron and Shire were the dominant breeds used in the north country in chilling the blood of the mustang.

About the same time, through the southwest a special type known as the Quarter Horse was used to breed cow horses. These "dash' 'horses probably came from the green mountain country; They carried a large amount of Thoroughbred blood in their veins. Steel Dust and Copper Bottom strains became known and generally were offspring of stallions by those names.

The coming of the horse changed the mode of living of the redskinned Indians. The Comanches were one of the first tribes to capture and ride horses. The use of horses to hunt game became popular. This activity led to invasions on other tribes' hunting grounds and resulted in fierce wars. The American Indian was a supreme horseman.

It is claimed that as early as 1730, the Nez Perce Indians assembled, bred, and improved the spotted horse, now known as the Appaloosa. This tribe bred only their best horses; they gelded and traded the poor ones to other less aggressive Indian clans. Today there are more than 34,000 owners of Appaloosa horses who have registered over 65,000 head. California alone boasts 10,366 registered Appaloosas, leading all states in the Union. At the National Appaloosa Horse Show in 1967, a total of 687 horses competed in various contests.

The versatile Thoroughbred breed is being used to improve the quality, speed, and courage of the Appaloosa. Such names as Miss Three Decks, Chargeono Bar and Alter Bar are found among the winners of this breed.

Horses are indispensable in many of man's modern activities. It is impossible to conduct and manage a modern cattle ranch without the use of horses. The jeep has not been able to replace the cow pony. Since there are 38,000 cattle ranches in California that carry about 4 million head of cattle, it is assumed that 114,000 horses are used in this business. A small number of draft horses are still used on many ranches for odd jobs that cannot be performed well by motorized equipment.

In the early days, before automobiles and tractors replaced the horse, this animal was raised on farms in the great agricultural areas of the Midwest. In the West, however, most of the horses were raised on the open range. It was not uncommon for some ranchers to specialize strictly in horse production. These range-raised horses possessed excellent feet and bone; because of the rough, rocky terrain in which they grazed, they were agile and sure-footed. Fewer diseases and parasites were present because of the large areas in which these horses roamed.

Many of the present-day horses are produced in urban areas. Under these cramped conditions, problems in nutrition and disease are more difficult to cope with and are more numerous than when these animals were produced on the farm or range. Therefore, the horse owner of today must have and take advantage of the knowledge available on nutrition, management, and disease control to be successful in raising the equine.

The last census report of the number of horses on farms in California was made in 1960, at which time there were 79,000 animals valued at $169 per horse. The State Department of Agriculture has discontinued inventoring this section of our livestock. This figure probably does not include horses in riding clubs located in cities, towns and communities.

During 1965, county farm advisors in California made a survey of the number of horses in each county. This figure indicated there were 200,979 head in the state which includes animals in riding clubs as well as those on farms. Some authorities claim that there are close to 300,00 horses in the golden state.

The aesthetic value of the horse is another important and valuable asset to man. This is one asset that is difficult to measure in dollars and cents. Indeed, the beauty of our state would be less without the horse. This animal adds attraction and interest.

The recreation value that horses bring to the population of California is difficult to measure. Sporting events, such as rodeos, horse shows, polo and racing, have a tremendous attraction. Probably these events, when grouped together, have a larger attendance than any other single sport in the state. The horse has an important role in all rodeo events both on the track and in the arena. In 1966, approximately 7 million persons paid to watch horse racing in all forms in California. Racing programs were conducted for a total of 571 days. In the U.S. more than 40 million went to races in 1966. It is estimated that more pepole watched horse racing than football or baseball games.

The horse is used in training our youth—both rural and urban— to become better citizens, thus curbing juvenile delinquency. Besides the hundreds of riding clubs established throughout the state, there are 150 to 200 4-H horse clubs, composed of 9500 members. About 782 unselfish local leaders help train these boys and girls in caring for and feeding horses, as well as better horsemanship. These clubs are located in 56 counties of California, with Los Angeles County having the largest membership. It is estimated that the value of these members' animals is 2.5 million dollars; that their tack and equipment are estimated at $250,000; that barns, corrals and other equipment have a value of about one quarter of a million dollars. It is fashionable for a person with a well-rounded education to have some knowledge of horses and horsemanship.

The largest monetary value of the horse industry for the State of California probably comes from racing. In 1966, a total of $39,247,166.90 was paid to the state treasury through taxes from the race track. Of this amount, county and district fairs received $9,287,045.67. The remainder of this tax money went into the general state fund. Those of you who enjoy going to fairs, stock and horse shows must give the horse considerable credit for helping maintain these educational and entertaining functions. Then, too, when your son or daughter attends some of the state-supported higher institutions of learning, it should be remembered that for years many of the tax dollars supporting these colleges and universities have been made available through horse racing. It is also easy to see that the equine helps to relieve the tough state tax problem.

The two breeds that are most important as far as numbers and value are concerned, and from the standpoint of recreation and furnishing equipment for operating ranches, are the Quarter Horse and the Thoroughbred. In 1967, California had 41,433 registered Quarter Horses. During 1966 there were 20 auction sales of Quarter Horses in California; the average price received was $1,052.

Go Man Go, sired by the great Thoroughbred stallion Top Deck, sold for $125,000 in 1962. Last year Rocket Bar, a registered Thoroughbred but primarily a Quarter Horse sire, recently sold for $470,000. Vessels Stallion Farm has sold four stallions for $100,000 or more. They are as follows: Scooper Chick, $100,000; Three Chicks, $100,000; Triple Chick, $100,000; and Alamitos Bar, $125,000.

In 1966 the American Quarter Horse Association organized and sponsored 1,239 horse shows in the U.S. and Canada. A total of 35,389 horses competed, an increase of 1,227 over 1965 and an increase of 3,481 over 1964.

The richest Quarter Horse purse is also the richest horse race in the world and is held at Ruidoso, New Mexico. The gross purse for the 1967 All American Futurity was $486,000 and netted the winner's owner $228,300.

Although the Quarter Horse breed is only 27 years old, it has grown to 444,721 registered animals at the end of 1966 and has made steady increases of 50,000 horses per year. This information gives some indication of the popularity of this breed of horse and the net worth of this industry.

The most popular bloodlines in the Quarter Horse breed today trace back to such Thoroughbred stallions as Three Bars, Top Deck, and Depth Charge, indicating the value of the Thoroughbred is developing light breeds of horses.

The Thoroughbred horse is said by some to be the most versatile of all breeds. Thoroughbreds have been used to improve most of our known light horse breeds, namely, American Saddle Horse, Standardbred, Quarter Horse, Appaloosa, and others. This breed boasts of having about 15,000 head registered in California. They are located on some 500 farms in 53 counties. About 7,500 of these are mares and 650 stallions. The net worth of this industry, which includes horses, buildings, equipment, land, etc., is estimated to be more than $200 million.

The California Thoroughbred Association has more than 700 members. It maintains a public library with over 4,000 volumes of literature pertaining to the horse. It publishes a fine monthly magazine and sponsors several auction sales each year.

In order to keep this great Thoroughbred horse industry running, the cost is approximately $25 million per year, itemized as follows:

```
$  4,000,000 - feed
  10,000,000 - payrolls
   6,000,000 - training fees
   2,000,000 - jockey fees
   1,500,000 - transportation
     500,000 - horse shoeing
     500,000 - veterinary services

INCOME
$13,000,000 - purses from racing
  1,600,000 - sales of horses
  2,600,000 - breeding fees
```

You will notice that there is a deficit between costs and income. The owners of these Thoroughbred establishments make up the difference. It costs about $5,000 per year to keep a horse in training.

Other breeds, such as Arabian, Morgan and the Standardbred, are also popular. The number of registered animals in these breeds in California ranks high as compared to other states.

The horse is a valuable research animal. Gonadotrophic hormones from pregnant mare serum and estrogenic hormones from the urine of these mares are used in human medicine. Pregnant mare serum, gonadotrophin, is used in stimulating ovarian activity in girls with delayed puberty. The estrogens in the urine are widely used in treatment of the menopause and other maladies in which the level of enstrogen is low.

Considerable income from this horse industry is from horse meat. It is difficult to estimate the total value of income from this source. Horses are worth about 8c a pound. There are seven licensed slaughterers for horses, mules, and burros in California. Products from these plants are not used for human consumption. These plants are located in the following counties: Alameda, Humboldt, Los Angeles, San Joaquin, San Luis Obispo, Sonoma, and Riverside. The horse is an important animal from the standpoint of the history of our state.

An attempt has been made to point out the importance of the horse to the welfare of the people of California. It is easy to see that this animal is of primary importance, not only from the standpoint of financial gain but also in furnishing aesthetic values, recreation, and helping our boys and girls to become better citizens. The horse serves us for research purposes, for the study of evolution, and supplies an important food in the form of meat. Any research that will improve the efficiency of this industry should have high priority in our colleges and universities.

Big Red — Man O'War Statue, Lexington, Kentucky

Kings of the Turf

Are you a lover of the king of sports? Do you enjoy watching the gallant Thoroughbreds circle the oval in keen competition for new records, high honors, and big purses? Well, if you are, you'll get a big kick out of reading about an imaginary matched race between three of the greatest running horses that ever looked through a bridle; namely, Man O' War, the big red runner of track history; Seabiscuit, the big little horse with the strong heart; and Whirlaway, champion money-winner and one of the strongest stretch runners of all time.

Take a deep seat in your easy chair, light up your favorite pipe, relax and try to picture these three outstanding stake winners in such a unique race. The scene is at Santa Anita in southern California, one of the most beautiful and up-to-date race tracks in the whole wide world. A purse of $150,000 goes to the winner of this mile and a quarter heart-breaking contest. The time is February 22, 1936. A racing crowd of over 100,000 has gathered to witness this colorful and history-making affair. They are tense, anxious, and a sporting, spending group. The gambling is heavy.

Each of the horses is 4 years of age, veteran campaigners of many of the major tracks of the country. They are in perfect shape and full of run. All have been trained well for this special history-making event. Man O' War will carry 133 pounds, top weight for any champion racer. Whirlaway will pack 130 pounds, and Seabiscuit only 127 pounds.

Tod Sloan, the big money-winning jockey is up on "Big Red," George "Ice-Man" Wolf is in the stirrups on Seabiscuit, and Eddie Arcaro is piloting the long-tailed Whirlaway. Man O' War is weighing 1,150 and is 16 hands high. His big red body looks fit to do the route in record time. Whirlaway is sleek and trim, and his heavy tail makes him look larger than his 1,060 pounds. The chunky, short-coupled Seabiscuit tips the beam to a full 1,000 pounds and appears no match for the other two large and natural-built runners.

As the three great idols of the king of sports parade proudly and arrogantly to the post, the band strikes up "America," and then the strains of "I Love You California" echoes throughout the palm and orange groves that surround the area. As the sweet notes of music float through the sunkissed air, they bring back fond memories of yesteryears when "Lucky" Baldwin and Leland Stanford were kings of racing strips around the world.

Clem McCarthy is calling the race and he has already announced that the Biscuit has number one position, Whirlaway number two, and old Man O' War number three. The Howard horse enters the starting gate first and stands quietly, Whirlaway comes in with a little coaxing and stands ready for the word. Man O' War is nervous, and as usual puts up a stiff fight before he enters the stall. Sam Riddle is worried about his runner for he rears and plunges and throws himself in the stall. Under expert handling, he is up and they lead him back in after about a 10-minute session.

The crowd is crying for the race to start and just then McCarthy yells, "They're off!" The "Biscuit," true to his kind, breaks on top, Man O' War second, and Whirlaway third. Howard has instructed his jockey to follow the Riddle entry closely, and Arcaro was told to let his champion runner run his natural race.

"Big Red" catches his grandson at the eighth pole and swings into the lead, throwing his head and crying to run. At the quarter, it's still "Big Red," and the time is 21 flat, a sizzling pace, but the "Biscuit" hangs on one length behind while Whirlaway is four lengths back but running smoothly and easily, Sloan keeps his mount in the lead and at the half he is clocked at 45.1, a blistering speed. Into the back stretch—Whirlaway is seven lengths behind his two rivals while the little bay horse lays right at the big sorrel's flank as they hit the sixth furlong stake at 1:09 flat. Just as the 1-mile post looms into sight, the "Biscuit" moves out into the lead and the timers clock him at 1.33-1/5, a record for this distance.

As they turn down the home stretch, that heart-breaking highway, Seabiscuit and Man O' War are running a dead heat. It's now that Whirlaway makes his move. He's coming up fast, closing the gap and proving once again his great, stretch-running ability. The crowd has gone panicky with excitement. The din and the noise are tremendous as these great Thoroughbreds charge down that clubhouse lane and into pay dirt.

Whirlaway's head is at Seabiscuit's flank, now at his shoulder and now just a neck behind his two great leaders. Sloan goes for his whip and the world's greatest running horse, Man O' War, shoots across the winning wire to be crowned the winner— just a bare neck ahead of his two strong running rivals. Whirlaway and Seabiscuit run a dead heat. The time? Well, it's a record— 1.59-3/5—made in true championship style by a real king of the turf, a true Thoroughbred.

Wildlife Trends

Top gunner — Ray Conway, cattleman, Grass Valley, Calif.
Courtesy Richard Teague

All of you Mother Nature lovers, lend me your ears. Let's turn back the pages of time 20 or 30 years and recall, if possible, the pleasant whistle of the mountain quail, the spectacular flight of the wild honker geese as they wedged through the sky in noisy tandem honking an indication that spring had come or that fall was fast approaching. Try to picture a band of Mallard ducks with their green heads shining in the sun as they fed contentedly in the slough below the barn, and a flock of mountain grouse as they thundered from under your feet to the limbs of a giant fir to watch you with curious eye from behind their needled fort. Where are the wild pigeons that one time darkened the heavens in their autumn flights to the acorn fields?

Yes, the drain on Mother Nature's feathered folk has been drastic and we who have spent some time in the open have to think hard to recall when we have last seen a real flock of these migratory sky fliers, or upland "song" birds.

We scratch our heads even harder to remember the time we last laid our searching eyes on a mighty mule buck, or the thrill we enjoyed snagging an old-time mess of trout. Not only the game of the sky but of the mountain stream have gone down before the long-barreled gun and sharp-barbed hook of white men, in affording them pleasure and satiating their killer instinct.

The happy hunting ground of the copper-skinned Indian is gone. The original dwellers of the mountain, plain, sky and stream are fast becoming blotted out because of man's greed to kill. I can think of nothing more shameful, heartbreaking and destructive than to have our marsh lands without ducks and geese; mountains and plains devoid of graceful deer; valleys and foothills without grouse and quail; troutless snow water streams; and skies with no feathered travelers going to and fro.

Man has always squandered nature's gift, and has been extravagant with his natural resources. Conservation of soil, water, minerals, timber and game is rather new compared to the destruction program of God's gifts to man.

Old time market hunters claimed that Monterey County had the largest quail population of any area in California. Two top upland game hunters, namely Jack Botts of Bradley, and Jan Martinus of Lockwood, maintain that during the 20's and 30's there were literally thousands of quail along the Nacimiento and San Antonio Rivers.

In the early 40's the military moved in on the Camp Roberts and Hunter Liggitt Reservations. Heavy uncontrolled hunting took place which virtually exterminated California's state bird from those areas. This, then, is a good illustration on what happens when man's greed to kill is not controlled.

I am partially convinced that the majority of the outdoor people of this country are cognizant of the full protection our wild life needs if it is to survive the advancement of civilization. Public sentiment is gaining momentum against the poacher, the game hog, the pot shooter, and the law breaker. The high-powered rifle and automatic scatter guns are going to be silenced in this rising tide against destruction and greed. Whether the farmers of this fair land like it or not, they are going to become more involved in this conservation movement. From all sides one hears the sportsmen shouting about how the land tiller can aid the serious situation by becoming more interested in the propagation of many kinds of game. They say, "The farmers own the land and it's up to them to protect their breeding places, furnish feed, and cooperate with state and federal agencies in the control of predatory animals. Then by strict enforcement of rigid laws on bag limits and regulated hunting, our wildlife will be forever perpetuated."

The farmers on the other hand have different ideas on the situation. They say, "What's the need for us to protect the game? We cannot be assured that they will receive full protection against poachers during the closed season. During open season we are inconvenienced almost every day by the so-called sportsmen wanting to hunt. If we allow hunting, we have no insurance against the game hog; the shooter who has no respect for our property, who leaves gates open, sets fires, kills and ruins our stock." This seems to be quite a general opinion among farmers. For instance, the cattlemen in the mule deer country maintain that they will be much better off when those beautiful big deer are all extinct. Each year thousands of hunters invade their ranges, camp at the choice springs, tramp through the mountains decked out in red hats and shirts promiscuously trying to stampede the stock off the ranges. Farmers estimate this costs them thousands of dollars each year.

Agriculturists claim the sportsmen have a bigger part to play in this saving of the wildlife than they have. How many hunters, they ask, after wounding a buck mortally but being unable to find it, tear up their tag and call it quits for the season, or, after dropping a quail or duck in a place they were unable to reach, called it part of their bag for the day? Many shooters kill more than the limit of game each year; they fill out the bag limit for a less successful friend, or after catching a limit of trout, keep on casting, throwing the small ones away, even though they are dead by that time. How about the duck hunter who plays poker all day yet goes home with a limit of ducks, and the pigeon hunter who fails to retrieve his bird because it fell in the madrone thicket a few hundred yards away instead of in the trail near his stand? This sort of murdering is costly to our game and is fast removing it from our land.

The animosity that exists between the landowner and the sportsmen regarding this serious game problem must be cleared up or the vicious killing will continue, resulting in the extinction of our most important game. Both sides must give and take. The sportsmen will have to stop their ruthless killing and disregarding the property rights of the farmer. The landowners and farmers will have to become more interested in the propagation of the game and the protection of the breeding places. He must help insure ample feed, and cooperate with other agencies in the control of predatory animals. In the Middlewest, the farmers are doing this and being paid for their efforts not only by receiving money for shooting privileges, but by the beauty and aesthetic value these animals and birds afford.

Unless these two factions can be brought together with a desire to work harmoniously for the good of our wild life, we may as well pull down the curtain and say "adios" to nature's game gift to man.

A Modoc mule deer trophy.

Long Live the King

The balances of nature, survival of the fittest, dog eat dog—you are no doubt familiar with these expressions. And, if you have a mountain background, you have probably heard stories about one snake killing and consuming another. Hard to believe? Yes. To see one of these scaley, agile reptiles wildly attack and completely kill and engulf a vicious, poisonous reptile is a scene very few people are fortunate enough to witness in a lifetime.

The battle I will try to describe to you was between a powerful, fast-moving, non-poisonous, black and white king snake and a flat-headed, deadly, venomous rattler. Long Valley in Southern Monterey County, California, was the setting for this primitive combat, which was witnessed by K. L. Eade, a rancher, his wife, and two friends.

Going into town on a bright June morning, Eade spied a three-foot rattler side-winding his way across the road just in front of the car. Eade jumped from the car and prepared to make a quick job of the snake. He found the rattler coiled and ready for battle. Grabbing a five-pound rock, he started to heave it just as he noticed the rattler's readiness for attack was not for him.

Four feet away from the sizzling rattler and seemingly sparring for an opening, aggressively advanced a king snake—easily recognizable by his well-known marking of black and white rings. This pinto reptile was moving cautiously but swiftly and surely toward the coiled rattler who lay with deadly fangs bared.

When the king had maneuvered to a point within 2 feet, the rattler struck—lightening is slow in comparison with the swiftness of that strike. The king, with unmatched speed, ducked his ugly head and clamped his mouth around the rattler's body about 6 inches back of the head. With a killer's murderous intent and speed, he wrapped numerous coils of his length around his poisonous enemy's body. Intense pressure was exerted by the king, and the rattler looked more than hopeless, yet he fought desperately for release. For a full 5 minutes the king held this terrific squeezing pressure on the rattler. Outside of a futile, dogged rattling, the rattler was helpless. Parts of his body were flattened almost completely by the intense stranglehold of the king snake. This alternate gripping and releasing of the rattler's body was kept up by the king for one-half hour. Dull, crunching sounds, then a faint rattle—were mute evidence that every rib in the rattlers body was being broken and crushed.

This rattler, true to his type, had a fighting heart and unbreakable spirit. Loosened finally by the king and lying as if dead, the rattler suddenly and surprisingly struck again, this time directly at the king's head. Instead of ducking, the striped snake met the rattler's charge, catching him firmly by the upper part of his mouth and working slowly until the whole flat head was in his mouth. After noisly chewing and crunching this head for a few moments, the king started to devour his poisonous enemy head first. As part of the rattler would slip down, the king would release some of his coils, and slide a small portion more into his great jaws. It took the king about an hour to finish this meal—only about 10 minutes to win the actual battle.

Thus ended another display of cannibalism—where one of man's most hated and feared enemies was the loser.

A sidewinder.

Hunting Stories

Lucking out — Julius Trescony, near Jiggs, Nevada

Many stories have been told around campfires, bunkhouses and mahogany bars regarding deer hunting. Over the years the following are some that have been kicked around when cattlemen assembled to celebrate a good rain, a wedding, or the birth of a son.

Cliff Hicks, good-looking, prominent cattleman of Santa Maria, California, tells this one.

"I was riding a green bronc up through the arroyo on the Santa Margarita Ranch one morning. I dismounted to open a wire gate and something told me to look up on the hillside. A fine 3-point buck was lying down with his head partly concealed by some sagebrush. I quickly jerked the gun from my scabbard, took aim at his head and fired. The buck rolled down the hill. I put the gun back in my scabbard and closed the gate and as I started to mount the skittish horse, I saw the buck running around the hillside.

"One of my top cowboys was in that vicinity, and I yelled to him that the buck was coming around the mountain. When he spied the buck, he shook out a loop in his rope, and since he was riding a fast horse, he quickly dabbed his loop on his horns. I rushed up with my rope, and the first throw caught both heels. We stretched him out there on the mountainside and slit his throat. The shot I had fired creased his horn right at the base of his head."

Several years ago, while hunting in Modoc County in the flatwoods near Hazleton Springs, Slicker Rice, Kid McWilliams and I decided to separate and see if each of us could get a shot at a legal deer. McWilliams was riding a mule. This hybrid animal, true to its traits, would not negotiate the brush alone. We wanted to follow my gray hunting horse.

As we proceeded through the snow brush and fir trees, Rice, shooting from the top of his Paiute mount, pumped four bullets in the direction of a 4-point mule deer. A few seconds later Mc-williams and I spied a 4-pointer standing by a tree. I jumped off and shot, and the deer fell. Mac said, "You got 'em." We tagged the deer, cleaned him, and hung him up in a sapling tree.

After this job had been completed, Rice came pacing up on his bay horse and asked, "Where is the buck I shot?" We informed him that we didn't know but there was a possibility that the one we hung in the tree might be his. Since the gun I fired was a 25-35 and Slicker's was a 30-30, it was easy to tell who had killed the deer. When a bullet from either of these guns is fired through the shoulders of a deer, it usually sticks in the skin on the opposite side. We quickly found the bullet, cut it out, and Lo and Behold! it fitted Rice's gun perfectly. Off came my tag; on went Rice's.

We had a consultation and decided perhaps another buck had been hit. Fortunately I had my excellent deer dog, Ring, with me, so we placed Rice and McWilliams on the outskirts of the area and I went up through the middle with my dog. We had not gone far until I could see that the dog had struck a fresh track. Immediately I told him to pursue the deer. He went only about 50 yards and started baying. McWilliams ran up, saw that it was a 3-point buck and shot the lower jaw off. For this feat we nick-names him "The Dentist."

Hardy Vestal, of Pittville, Lassen County, California, likes to tell this story about his deer dog.

Late one fall he was hunting in the Dixon Butte country north of the muddy Pit River. Late one evening he jumped a mighty mule buck carrying 6 points on each side. He dismounted, and after several shots at long distance broke a front leg on the deer. On being wounded, the deer started downhill over the Guthrie Bluff, heading for Pit River. Vestal, on his half-Thoroughbred horse and with his trusty spotted shepherd dog, purused him. As the deer hit the banks of the river he jumped in and started swimming across. While the deer was in the middle of this muddy stream, Hardy shot, killing the deer. The dog, showing the courage and steel true to the shepherd breed, jumped in the water, swam to the deer, and then brought him back to the bank.

A few years ago, Julius Trescony of San Lucas and I were hunting deer near Coyote Lakes at the foot of the Copped Mountains, Elko County, Nevada. William B. Wright, owner of the property,, instructed us to go to their headquarters at Coyote Lakes and contact his foreman, Lee Ewing, with instructions that Ewing would guide us to the best buck hunting country in all of Nevada.

We arrived there early on a cold October morning as Ewing was rounding up his remuda. We handed him the letter of instructions, but he didn't read it, saying that if Bill Wright sent us that was all that was necessary. He asked us if we had our chairs with us, meaning saddles. When we said, "Yes," he looked at Trescony and asked him if he could ride a snaffle bit horse. Julius thought that he might be able to fork a Nevada broomtail of this training. This steel-blue-eyed mountain man looked at me and said, "I have only one horse that doesn't buck, and I ride him myself."

We finally saddled up, gathered up our hunting gear, opened the gate of this big round corral, and headed for buck country on a long fast trot known only to the Nevada cattleman.

After trotting for about 2 miles, Trescony turned to me and said, "This is no way to hunt deer."

I said to him, "Are you complaining? Remember, you are a guest."

On reaching the top of one of the high peaks, Ewing ordered us to get off our horses and start hunting. We walked around through some mahogany and in a few minutes Ewing ordered us back on our horses. If he knew diplomacy, he wasn't using it on these Californians. As we rode out into an opening he said, "There's your buck."

I looked over my left shoulder and there stood a 4-point buck. I jumped off and shot, and the deer ran away. Ewing said,

"What's the matter with that California gun? Doesn't it shoot straight?"

I said, "I don't know."

He said, "Shoot at that rock over there." I shot at the rock and hit it, and he was convinced the gun was all right.

We went up to where the deer had been standing and found that he had been slightly wounded. Since there were so many deer in that country, Ewing decided that we would not track the deer but hunt for fresh ones.

We trotted for another mile and we came to a long ridge, and here our guide told us that we were to separate. One was to go with him on the left of the rim and the other on the right side. Julius chose to go with Ewing. I proceeded alone. After we had been parted for about 20 minutes, I heard two shots and said to myself, "Julius has probably got a buck because when he points a gun it's usually in the right direction."

A few minutes later Ewing appeared on the top of this rocky, rough rim on his top mountain horse where only a goat could go and asked me if I'd seen a deer come into that area. I told him "No." He laughed and said, "Your partner missed a big one." I proceeded on around the hill and a big 8-point buck jumped out of some sagebrush and I planted three out of four shots into his huge body. He fell like many of Joe Louis' opponents. Before I could reach the carcass of the deer, Ewing was there on his big black horse telling me that I'd killed the biggest deer in the woods. I rode up and asked him if I could help him prepare the deer to be carried out. His instructions were, "Don't touch the deer, you might learn something."

After the deer was dressed, he looked up at my saddle and said, "Is that rope any good?" I said, "Yes, why?" He said, "I wasn't sure because it was from California." We put the rope around the deer's antlers and he dragged it down the hill to a suitable mahogany tree and hung it up for the night. We trotted on to camp.

About a mile from camp, Trescony said to me, "This is the roughest damn horse I ever rode." I said, "Are you complaining again?" He said, "No, but since you claim to be an expert on horses, I thought you might want to take a good look at a rough horse."

The next day bright and early, we started back in the mountains with Ewing's famous pack mule to bring out this monarch of the woods. He informed us that he could load any deer in this woods on his mule alone, and proceeded to demonstrate it. After it was tied on, we started home according to custom—on the trot. Being very anxious to get this set of antlers home without being broken, I was somewhat concerned as to whether it would fall off while the mule was trotting. I said, "Lee, stop the mule, the deer is going to fall off."

He said, "No it won't," and trotted faster.

I said, "God dammit to hell, Lee, it's going to fall off!"

He said, "No it won't," and I said, "What the hell is going to hold it on?"

He replied, "Gravity, son, gravity," and we went on into camp.

Harold Eade, his hunting dog and trophy.

Pioneer judgment — William John Albaugh, age 83, McArthur, Calif.
                                        Courtesy George Ingram

The Boss

My father, William John Albaugh, was born in Pennsylvania on March 23, 1867. His early life was spent on a small farm, where he learned the principles of hard work and initiative which form the character of those who live close to the land.

At the age of 17, he was lured West by tales of buffalo hunting and Indian wars. On his way westward in 1886, he mingled with the cowboys and the cattle barons in Dodge City, which was then considered to be the cattle center of the West. Most of his early traveling was done by riding the rods.

In 1893 he settled in Fall River Valley, and a few years later became engaged in the beef cattle business. In 1896, he married Wilhemina Baker, a gentle, loving, and generous native daughter of California. To this union was born six children, four sons and two daughters.

My mother was known far and wide in the north country for her friendliness and fine hospitality. She was a splendid cook and enjoyed preparing dinners for friends and relatives. She received real pleasure from organizing and holding family reunions. This was her method of holding the family together and it worked.

My dad was a strong disciplinarian. He ruled with an iron hand, you might say. In spite of this, he was highly respected by the entire family. He taught his family how to work, a lesson that was valuable throughout their lives.

During his busy life he acquired several ranches and built up a herd of 700 head of high-producing Hereford cattle. His farming operations have been said to be among the most diversified in Northern California. He was active in community work, having been a member of the local school board, and was interested in furthering higher education. He greatly admired Parker Talbot, first Farm Advisor of Shasta County, saying he was a builder of men. He was one of the first directors of the California Farm Bureau in Shasta County and took an active part in the improvement of the Redding-Alturas highway.

He was one of the leaders in the case between the Pit River farmers and a large power corporation over water rights on the Pit and Fall Rivers. The ranchers won this case!

He organized the Fall River Livestock Association and served as its first president; he was also a director of the California Cattlemen's Association for over a quarter of a century.

Some of his unusual sayings were:

"If you have an appointment with someone and you find you cannot be on time, then be 10 minutes early!"

"Anyone can start a project, but it takes a good man to finish it."

When things got tough, he would say, "Don't give up; that's the time to hang on because that's when the other fellow is ready to let go."

"You don't need to know much to get by, providing you know how to use what you know."

"If you want to test a man's character, put him 2,000 miles from home, broke!" (This was a harsh way to assess one's capabilities.)

My dad was strong for diversification. He said, "I had something to sell everyday."

William John Albaugh began his life 84 years after the establishment of the U.S. as an independent nation. His 91 years covered a span of time that saw more than one-half of the history the American Republic in its most turbulent and rapidly-expanding period. It encompassed the period which witnessed the near-extermination of the buffalo, the long spectacular cattle drives, the daring Pony Express riders, and the completion of the transcontinental railroad; the invention of barbed wire, the settlement of the West and the closing of the American frontier, and the longest period of peace in American history. His life began when Andrew Johnson, the vice-president who had assumed the office of the presidency after the assassination of Abraham Lincoln, was in office as the 17th president, and ended in the Atomic and Space Age, during the administration of Dwight D. Eisenhower, the 33rd President of the U.S.

From Rigs to Riches

Inventive genius — R. C. Baker, Sr., Coalinga and Whittier, Calif.
Courtesy Mrs. George Anderson

When Reuben Carlton Baker, my mothers brother and thus my uncle, left the beautiful Fall River Valley in 1894 for greener pastures, he had a deep and burning desire to accumulate enough wealth so he would be independent when he became old and feeble. This Cinderella boy, before he laid down his tools in 1958 at the age of 87, had established a corporation that returned over $1,000,000 a month. In addition to this, he formed the R. C. Baker Foundation with a million dollars in assets, the earnings to be used for education and research purposes.

Carl, as he was affectionately known by his relatives and wide circle of friends, was born in 1872 in old "Virginny' near the historical town of Harper's Ferry. He was the fourth child of Reuben and Sarah Baker, Quaker stock from the state of Pennsylvania. His father was a Civil War veteran and had the distinction of marching with Sherman on that devastating trek from Atlanta to the Sea. At the tender age of 2 he migrated with his family to Shasta County near the City of Redding. After a few years at this location, they moved to Fall River Valley in Northeastern Shasta County, near Pittville, a small town located on the banks of the muddy Pit River. It was here that he received his schooling in a one-room country school. Later a 3-months hitch at a Business College in Stockton completed his education. While growing to manhood in this isolated community, he learned to till the soil, care for livestock, and take part in community activities.

Mountain folks in those days provided their own entertainment and horse racing was a favorite sport on Sunday afternoons. Carl owned a little brown Thoroughbred mare called Daisy. He rode her in the races bareback and was the champion jockey in that area.

In the roaring 80s farming was considered to be in the "bare handed" age. Farm work was drudgery because there were no improved machinery to handle the heavy work; thus agriculture did not appeal to him. He was restless and eager to enter the industrial world. When he was 21 years of age, there was a gold boom in Alaska and oil had been struck in large quantities in the Los Angeles area. In order to make a decision as to whether to be a gold miner or an oil magnate, he stuck a stick in the ground and said, "if it falls north, I'll go to Alaska and if the southern direction, I'll head for the black gold fields." It tumbled to the north.

This farm boy immediately rolled his bed and went over the mountain to Redding. He secured a job in a stone quarry for $2 a day. When he went to get his clothes at the end of 2 weeks someone had stolen them. Lacking funds for the Alaskan trip, he purchased a ticket to Los Angeles, where he secured a job hauling oil for $2 a day. This future oil magnate climbed the ladder in the oil business rapidly going from an expert tool dresser to an efficient and capable cable tool driller. He soon went into partnership with Irving Carl. This partnership drilled 20 wells near Depth Street in Los Angeles. Later he drilled his own well and sold it for $5,000. This gave him enough money to pay all of his bills and own his own drilling rig. In 1897, he trekked back to Fall River Valley and married Minnie Zumwalt, a neighboring cattleman's daughter. To this union was born a daughter, Thelma, and a son, Carlton.

In 1899 because of ill health (he was plagued with asthma most of his life) he moved to Coalinga, Fresno County. He continued drilling wells and at the same time managing other oil company properties. He gained a reputation of being one of the most astute oil drillers in the West.

It was in the Coalinga area, while drilling wells, that he was confronted with the problem of getting the casing down the fresh drilled hole. This was because of the unusual formation of the soil. He developed an offset bit, which enabled him to drill the hole larger than the casing. This became his first patent. Four years later, he invented the famous Baker casing shoe. This was a real foundation upon which he began to build a worldwide oil tool specialty business, known as the Baker Oil Tool Incorporated.

When Carl laid his drawing board and calipers aside in 1958, he had 124 U.S. and 12 foreign patents, all relating to the oil drilling business. Most of them had to do with sub-surface equipment. In addition to these inventions he and his co-inventors had registered 142 U.S. and 29 foreign patents. All of these patents have been assigned to Baker Oil Tools, Incorporated, without charge.

When this genius tool inventor was asked how he created these profitable and far reaching ideas, he stated, "I create practically all of my inventions while I lie in bed at night. I don't get up to make any notes, but take a few days to mentally work out the details, then I make a sketch and turn it over to my engineers for reproduction."

Although Carl Baker made Coalinga his main home, he drilled wells and investigated oil properties in Bakersfield, Texas, and Wyoming. He was a tower of strength in his community, having been mayor, member of school boards, highway commission, active in the Chamber of Commerce and other civic organizations. The original Baker Casing Shoe Company building was deeded to the City of Coalinga and is an outstanding museum displaying many relics of the oil business as well as the old and colorful West.

Everything that this oil tool genius touched turned to money. From 1901-20, he owned two large ranches in San Joaquin Valley, Coalinga Gas and Power Company, The First National Bank of Coalinga, Coalinga Theater, the Coalinga Western Oil Company and Coalinga Petroleum Company. All of these enterprises he sold at a profit.

The following is his formula for accumulating wealth for old age security.

1. Spend LESS than your income.
2. Invest all surplus funds in good, safe securities.
3. Always finish the job you start and then start another.
4. Invest all surplus funds for income—not for speculation.
5. Always live within your income—PAY AS YOU GO.
6. Never borrow money, unless you are sure of a profit.
7. Always be honest with yourself (and all others).
8. Consider all people honest (but remember some are not).
9. Always seek good advice for your investments.
10. Always re-invest the income from your investments.

He loved life and took special note of important milestones as shown by the following quotations:

> "The most progressive period the world has ever known has been during my 87 years of life. I remember my first telephone, the first electric light, the first electric motor, the first talking machine, the first automobile, the first airplane, the first moving pictures, the first radio, the first wireless telegraph, the first television, the first gas engine, and many other firsts that are too numerous to mention."

The accomplishments that this Fall River Valley farm boy made, strongly documents the fact that he was not only a genius when it came to inventing tools for drilling oil wells, but that he was an astute and capable business man as well. This is a combination difficult to equal and impossible to surpass. He was generous, modest, mild mannered, frugal and his actions and dress did not depict a millionaire. He refused to stay in hotels that employed a door man, saying that he could open his own doors. He did not drink nor smoke and was reluctant to patronize restaurant-bar establishments, saying that the lights were too dim to see what he was eating.

Carl Baker was a staunch Republican, a real patroit, honest, and sincere, as the day is long. You could trust him with uncounted gold.

If fate had directed him to the frozen wastes of Alaska, there is no question but what he would have been crowned with fame with the aid of the pick, pan and the shovel. On the other hand, had he remained on the land, with his inquisitive, searching mind, he no doubt would have invented equipment and machinery equal in importance to that of the wheel, the plow, and the horseshoe.

In my book, he was a top hand—a real champion, and as Western as the setting sun. Although he didn't wear the western hat nor the jingling spur—oil and cattle go together. You may have heard this as said by the Texas cowman, "My old cows sure produce when they rub on them there oil derricks."

The Pit River flooding.

THE BIG FOUR

Rob Flournoy, Vice President, California Cattlemen's Association
John Baumgartner, Past President, California Cattlemen's Association
J. Edgar Dick, Past Secretary, California Cattlemen's Association
Walter Rodman, Former Manager, California Beef Council

Gentleman John

No matter how you cut the descriptive cloth, John Baumgartner, Jr., of San Juan Bautista, California will emerge as the most popular and highly respected cattleman who ever pulled on a pair of boots. Always poised, gifted with a warm, magnetic personality, handsome, courteous, well mannered, an excellent host, John has often been referred to by his compatriots as a well-mounted "top gentleman" of the cattle business.

To document this stout statement, during his recuperation from a recent serious accident, this convivial rancher received thousands of cards, letters, telegrams as well as telephone calls from people in many walks of life. Some of the writers of these get-well messages were only casual acquaintances of John's, yet because of his widely-known contributions to the advancement of society, they were anxious to wish him a speedy and full recovery.

John Baumgartner has an interesting typical American-German-Irish "pedigree" and demonstrates the fact that inheritance comes from both parental lines. He is a grandson on his mother's side of Richard O'Neill, a Bostonian who came to San Francisco in 1850 and became a well-known meat packer and cattle rancher. John Clay, in his book "My Life on the Range" describes O'Neill as a brilliant student of the cattle business. Clay compared O'Neill with the late Henry Miller in his astuteness in cattle ranching. In 1882 Richard O'Neill in partnership with J. C. Flood purchased the 250,000-acre Santa Margarita ranch that lies between San Juan Capistrano Mission and San Diego. John's father was a reputable architect. With this type of background, it is easy to see why John demonstrates a love for cattle, outstanding managerial ability, attention to order and detail and many other qualities associated with distinguished leadership.

John, Jr., was born in San Francisco after the turn of the century. The first 9 years of his life were spent on the Santa Margarita ranch as well as during his vacations while attending high school and college. It was on this great cattle spread north of the border down Mexico way that John learned from the Indian cowboys to ride, rope and handle cattle as well as speak Spanish. During this period the ranch carried on a mixed operation, consisting of cows, calves, and selling three and four-year-old steers.

John went to Lowell High School and the University School of San Francisco, before entering the University of California at Davis, where he majored in animal science, graduating in 1925. While at UCD he was active in student affairs, having been a member of the livestock judging team, president of the student body and chairman of the student welfare council. In discussing his experiences at UCD, John stated that being on a judging team assisted him in developing decision-making talents. That year the UC judging team won first place at the Pacific International Livestock Show. John praised Dr. Elmer Hughes, saying he was one of the best coaches in the Western College Division. "The most valuabe lesson I learned in college," John said, "was to think clearly and get along with my fellow man."

In reminiscing about outstanding alumni, Dr. James H. Meyer, Chancellor, UCD, had this to say, "The first time I met John Baumgartner was when he acted as Grand Marshall for the UCD picnic day parade. He carried out this assignment with all the pride and dignity of a loyal alumnus. During my various administrative assignments on the UCD campus, John has been exceedingly helpful in suggesting new research projects and improving the image of the university among the taxpayers of California."

After graduation, this livestock leader spent a hitch working in a slaughterhouse, but soon returned to his first love, the Santa Margarita ranch, where he worked as an ordinary cowhand. "In those days," John stated, "a college cowboy was not looked upon with favor by ranch managers. They were of the opinion that too much book 'learnin' was not conducive to profitable cattle ranching.

In 1927, Baumgartner struck out on his own and went to San Benito County. Here he rented the Perle ranch in the Gabilan mountains and later the Avilla and Hedges ranches near San Juan Bautista. He ran stocker cattle on these properties and Ki Silacci, prominent cattlemen of Salinas, was of great help to him and became a very close friend.

While assisting with the original San Bautista benefit show in 1930 John met Elinor Lermen, whom he married in 1932 at the height of the depression. Elinor was a great community worker, assisting with the Junior League to raise money for charity. She also played the piano and sang for the early San Juan benefit shows. The Baumgartners have two children, a daughter and son, and six grandchildren.

By 1934, the depression — plus old man drought — had caused many cattlemen to go broke. And John, operating a speculative feeder business, joined the procession. Reminiscing about those New Deal days, John said, "I bought 340 head of steers at 10 cents a pound, and sold most of them at between 4 and 5 cents a pound. This minus-margin selling put too much red ink in the ledger and I went broke."

In August 1934 John found employment with the University of California as an Emergency Assistant Farm Advisor in San Benito County. Because of the falling economy, and widespread drought, the government had provided additional money for a nationwide livestock buying program to cull the herds closely, save feed and raise the price of livestock. He remained with the University for two years and then, with Taylor Pillsbury as a partner, operated the Las Cimas and Elkhorn ranches in San Benito County.

Following World War II John purchased a ranch in Santa Clara County near San Martin. This property was later sold and he purchased the Henry Petersen ranch in the Cottonwood district. Here he also operated a neighboring Brown's Valley ranch as well as the Bob Law ranch near Paicines.

In 1968 John sold the Petersen ranch, purchased part of the original Hedges ranch, and returned to live in San Juan Bautista where he had run cattle back in 1927. He now runs about 1,000 Hereford cattle in San Benito County, summering some in Oregon, and sells weaner calves in the fall. The bulls used for the development of this herd were purchased from Floyd Bidwell, Hat Creek, California. Because of the quality and performance ability of John's weaner calves, they usually bring a premium on the market.

John has cooperated on projects with the University of California many times, including the loan of his replacement heifers for an extensive study of an abortion-causing disease called vibriosis. Dr. John Kendrick, working with Farm Advisor Bud Beckley, was the U.C. Veterinarian in charge. Also interested in young people he helped Rocky Lydon organize a county-wide Future Farmer and 4-H Club Cow Palace feeder calf program.

During the past quarter of a century, John Baumgartner has been president of many state and county organizations. Furthermore, he has been chairman of numerous important national and statewide committees. All of these activities have been directed to the betterment of the cattle business and the advancement of higher education. For example, he was president of the California Cattlemen's Association during 1951-53. During that time he perfected the idea of holding demonstrations on improved practices in beef cattle production in connection with the annual cattlemen's association field meetings. This was done in cooperation with the Agricultural Extension Service. This project had a double-barreled effect by increasing attendance and boosting membership. John often said he did not know whether the cattlemen in northern California were the most efficient producers, but they were the best informed of any group in the West.

John was instrumental in organizing the San Benito County Cattlemen's Association and served as its first president. This is one of the strongest and most active county associations in California.

While a member of the State Board of Forestry and chairman of the Recreational Committee for the state cattlemen's association, he battled long and hard for the principle of multiple land use. Foresight told him that with the population explosion sooner or later even private land would eventually have to be used for other purposes — multiple land use — grazing alone would not be enough. He further reasoned that cattle and production of wildlife could be compatible and profitable.

John often outlined what he considered fundamental for an ideal organization. First, it had to be sound financially, have ample membership and capable leadership, and possess a program which would emphasize projects including legislation, education and promotion.

Because of his leadership and other guiding qualities, in 1957 he was chosen by a committee of the San Francisco Chamber of Commerce as "Livestock Man of the Year."

Other agricultural activities in which he has been involved include: Chairman, California Beef Council; past president, 33rd agricultural district; past chairman, University of California Livestock Advisory Committee (past chairman of the Commodity committee for this group); past chairman of the California Cattlemen's Association Public Relations, Recreation and Labor Relations committees; past chairman of the Landowner Recreation committee for the American National Cattlemen's Association; past chairman of Livestock and Meat Marketing conference in California; president, San Benito County Saddle Horse Association; director of California Rodeo in Salinas; chairman of Pageant and Rodeo of San Juan Bautista; member of Board of Trustees of National Cowboy Hall of Fame and Western Heritage Center.

John is an expert horseman — a reata and hackamore man. He is always well mounted and enjoys jackpot roping with his friends and neighbors. (At the San Benito County Saddle Horse Show in 1955 he and Henry Strohn won the championship in team roping.) Other hobbies include vigorously participating in community and civic far-reaching activities, such as: director of Hollister National Bank and Production Credit Corporation of Salinas; San Juan Bautista Historical and Museum Association; member of California State Park Advisory Board, members of Advisory Committee of Bank of California in Hollister; member of Hollister Elks Lodge and Knights of Columbus and Pacific Union Club in San Francisco; member of Fiesta Rodeo committee in San Juan Bautista; past Cub Scoutmaster in Hollister.

During John's busy and successful life he has kept two objectives in mind. One was to be a successful cattleman and the other was to give unstintingly of his time, energy and money to causes devoted to encourage more efficient agriculture through science and education. His deep desire is to contribute to knowledge so that the human race would move a little further forward and man can live more abundantly.

Words are yet to be penned that will fully appraise John's personality and character, but his greatest quality is that of making and keeping friends. To quote Thomas Hughes, "Blessed are they who have the gift of making friends for it is one of God's best gifts. It involves many things, but above all, the power of going out of one's self and appreciating whatever is noble and loving in another."

John's corral of friends are valuable and precious wealth, and we are glad to be a part of his riches!

Cattlemen's Cattleman — Jim G. Bardin, Salinas, Calif.

Top Hand

Jim G. Bardin of Salinas, Monterey County, is one of the most highly respected and prominent cattlemen who ever sat in a saddle. His grandparents were from the deep south (South Carolina). With an urge to roam and to better their lot in life, they migrated to the golden state, going the tough, hard way, through the yellow-fever laden swamps of the Isthmus of Panama. The year was 1856. Although this was only 8 years after John Marshall picked up the yellow pebbles at Colma, they were not seekers of the yellow dirt.

They immediately engaged in the cattle business, grazing their animals in the sand hills west of Salinas (now Fort Ord), in Carmel Valley and on the Salinas plains. The magnetic and colorful Bardin name has been closely associated with the history and improvement of the cattle business for 126 years. Jim's father purchased his present cattle ranch from the late Jesse D. Carr. This ranch located in the "Gabilan Range" includes part of Fremont's peak. This is an historical spot since the first American flag of possession that ever fluttered in the California breeze was hoisted here by Captain John C. Fremont in 1846.

Jim, a Stanford University graduate in economics, took over the full management of the ranch at the death of his father in 1932. During the past 38 years he has been very active, not only in community and civic affairs, but also on many worthwhile projects of benefit to the cow business.

He was instrumental in organizing the Monterey County Cattlemen's Association and was its first president. This is one of the leading cattle organizations in California. In 1938 he was chosen by the California Cattlemen's Association to represent the State of California on the Swift Tour. This event, which is sponsored by one of the "big five" in the meat packing industry, was to study marketing and merchandizing of meat on the eastern seaboard.

This prominent cattleman has been an excellent cooperator with the Agricultural Extension Service of the University of California. He was the first cattleman in California to use the strain 19 vaccine experimentally for the control of Brucellosis in beef cattle. Treating calves with this vaccine is a practice widely used today. In 1942 he demonstrated that 2-year-old beef steers could be successfully finished for slaughter on irrigated pasture by supplementing them with 4 or 5 pounds barley per head per day. That year his 55-acre irrigated pasture field produced 955 pounds of beef per acre, which was a record at that time. Two other early projects on beef cattle feeding carried out by Jim were to determine the value of fish meal as a protein supplement, and the feeding value of a complicated mineral mixture in a fattening ration for beef cattle.

Presently the Bardin Ranch runs about 400 breeding cows consisting of straight Hereford and Angus-Hereford crossbreds. Heifers are bred to calve at 20-24 months of age and bulls are rotated during the breeding season in order to bunch and increase the calf crop. Replacement heifers are selected mostly on weight per day of age.

Jim has been director of the California rodeo for 36 years. He has served on the arena committee and on the executive committee of his organization. He has been a director of the California Cattlemen's Association for 10 years and serves on the important legislative, water resources, and executive committees of this organization. For many years he has served as a director of Farmer's Mercantile Company, one of the largest International Harvester dealers in California. For the past 14 years he has been president of this organization.

In addition to these state and county activities, this busy cattleman has served in various positions on the following committees and organizations: (1) Council of California Growers; (2) County Charter-Study Committee; (3) Foreman of Grand Jury; (4) County Air Pollution Committee; (5) Director and President of Monterey County Tax Council; (6) First President of Salinas Valley Stanford Club; (7) Presently Vice-Chairman of Salinas Valley Water Advisory Commission; (8) Presently Director of Chamber of Commerce and Chairman of Water Committee.

Jim Bardin is known in cattle circles as an outstanding leader, renowned for his honesty and integrity. His word is as good as gold. He is always ready and willing to give time, money, and energy to worthwhile projects that will advance the cow business and make the community a better place in which to live. It is men like Jim who possess these rare and intangible traits that have made America great. Jim's lovely and radiant wife, Mary, is also a crusader in her own right for the improvement of the cattle business. She is past president of the Monterey County Cow Belles. She is legislative chairman for the California Cow Belles, president of the California Cow Belles and serves on Governor Reagan's Recreation Trails Advisory Committee.

Their son, Bob, is studying farm management at "Cal Poly."

Bill Casey's Chivaree

A man the world around — William Casey, San Lucas, Calif.

Back in the Democratic "New Deal Thirties" when Franklin Delano Roosevelt had a firm grip on the government's executive ribbons, Bill Casey, widely known as an expert horseman, top cattleman and hunter supreme, was the most eligible bachelor from Long Valley. Pretty Marie Musso was the popular school "marm" of nearby San Lucas. Southern Monterey County neighbors were highly elated when the two were joined in the holy bonds of matrimony.

Following the festivities after this well- and favorably-known couple were married, Kenneth Eade, son of big "Wes"—a top hand on the platform or horse and pride of that famous cattle family—promptly organized a surprise party and chivaree in honor of Bill and Marie. The big event was held at San Lucas, and where else but in the "loft" of Loren Bunte's store. Friends and relatives from far and near came loaded with gifts, bountiful foods, and "good cheer" to celebrate the happy occasion. Included, too, were out-of-county notables, even the famed and renowned Bert Sooy, the ex-blacksmith, cattleman and noted attorney, long a champion of the cowman's rights.

Soon was announced the Grand March, led, of course, by handsome Bill and his gracious, petite Marie. Thus was set the stage of an all-night party; dancing, merrymaking, and much toasting of the bride and groom from one and all.

As the clock on the wall struck 12, Kenneth Eade, in his friendliest yet polite manner, ascended the platform. The drummer in the orchestra beat a noisy fanfare. The attention of the merry crowd finally was captured. Kenneth proudly introduced Bert Sooy, the man who single-handed and with the grip of total depression over the land, succeeded in forming the state and government-aided plans for financing and erection of the present "Cow Palace" in San Francisco. And Bert succeeded, too, in organizing the now well-known Grand National Livestock Show. Bert Sooy was asked to address the celebrants on this festive occasion.

In that experienced and suave manner which comes to those with a full knowledge of law backed up by many good years of successful practice, Bert paid glowing tribute to the newlyweds. Well did he point out the joy and importance of Marie and Bill's marriage to their host of friends throughout the community. He summarized his speech with emphasis saying that Bill Casey was a real man, and a man so known and accepted in Long Valley could be a man the world around.

After more speeches and eulogies, the dancing and merriment continued. Kenneth Eade decided that it was time for some of the men to have their "liquid refreshments' alone. Under his guidance and direction, Bert Sooy, Ade Ansberry, Tom Thwaits, and yours truly with Kenneth slipped out of the "loft" to Hank Madson's bar. As we approached the well-known and old-time saloon, the din and noise drifted through the open door, depicting activities well underway inside. Several had already preceded us to Hank's "water hole."

As we entered the smoke-laden room, some of the local cowboys were lounging at the bar, partaking of Han's firewater, swapping tall stories of the day, and each relating his manly accomplishments. A quartet of the cowpokes were playing poker at one of the rickety, whiskey-stained card tables. Back at the far wall of the barroom sat Wes Eade, prominent cattleman of southern Monterey County. With him was George Mee, formerly of Arizona and later Los Angeles, but now the recent purchaser of, and new resident on, the famed Peach Tree Ranch. This township-sized piece of dirt at one time was owned and operated by that "Cattle King of the West," Henry Miller. Wes, too, long held the reputation for having bought and sold more cattle than any one ranchman residing in Monterey County. Wes in his time wrote few letters, attended few stockmen's meetings, and read only occasional livestock papers and journals. Yet he was known for many years as the shrewdest cowman in those parts on livestock markets and the trend of economic conditions. Over a neighborly "glass" these two respected and successful cowmen had been dickering most of the evening on a cow trade of some sort. As our group edged up to the rail, where men soon become tranquil and friendly, both Wes and George came over to greet us, extending their usual outstanding western hospitality.

Behind the bar was Hank Madson. Hank was a unique liquor dispenser. He was known far and wide over that part of the country as a man who always bought a round for every round of drinks purchased from him. Hank included himself with all of his drinking customers as well. Soon he was in the back room busy replenishing his bar supplies. Bert Sooy filled in behind the bar and began serving more drinks. No orders were taken for Bert just pushed full pint bottles of "Old Quaker" whiskey to each of our happy group. Everyone now well served, the toasts to the Caseys were begun anew.

At the end of the bar two cowhands suddenly tangled in a fistic brawl. No one interfered in their private fight. For several interesting minutes, they battled furiously and relentlessly on pretty even terms. Tables were overturned, chairs were broken and the whole building trembled under the impact of their rough and tumble fighting. Finally the shorter and more husky battler connected with a devastating left hook to the midsection. His opponent doubled up on the floor against the old brass rail of the bar. Sensing quick victory, the other jumped on his victim and began to bash the limp victim against the rail.

Then Wes Eade reacted immediately. He banged his glass of whiskey down on the mahogany bar with such force the contents splashed "plumb" to the ceiling. He was over the pair at once, grabbing the aggressor by the nape of the neck, and literally tore the two fighters apart, throwing one into the back wall, smashing him through the thin partition to Hank's private conference room. No unfair tactics could be tolerated. In a vehemently authoritative voice, Wes ordered the two fighters not only to vacate the saloon right now but to keep moving and leave town. Each of them in a taciturn manner picked up his few scattered belongings that had been lost during the grim and bloody struggle, then each respectfully shook hands with Wes Eade, thanking him for stopping the fight, and silently limped outside into the cold December night.

Yes, Wes Eade was champion of San Lucas again that night, as he had so often been over the past many years. As Ade Ansberry later stated, "In his heyday no one ever pushed Wes around, be it in a cow trade or fist fight."

The party soon was over. After much handshaking and good-byes, the chivaree for the Caseys so ended in the wee morning hours.

As Tom Thwaits, Bill Twisselman and I with our wives drove back to Salinas in the early hours of the morning through fog and cold wind, we discussed and rehashed in detail all events of that wonderful evening. One and all agreed that only those grand people of the southern Monterey County area could originate, organize and execute such a fine old-time chivaree. We were also in accord that probably we had seen that night one of the last of the real old-time barroom fights, the kind so common in those glorious days when the West was young.

Such was the night of Bill Casey's chivaree.

The Mee family, Tom, Mrs. and George.

"The Chief"

A leader of men — B. H. Crocheron, Berkeley, Calif.

B. H. Crocheron, late director of the Agricultural Extension Service of the University of California, was a tower of strength unequalled among the rural people of California and within the "Halls of Learning" of one of the greatest universities in the world.

"The Chief," as he was known to thousands who lived on the land, was truly an outstanding man in his field during this generation. He was deeply imbued with that pioneer spirit that "only the deserving shall be blessed and that no one shall get anything for nothing."

For these cardinal principles he fought long and hard. His heart went out to the people who tilled the soil, who lived on the land, and created the only new wealth known to man. They were the backbone of this great democracy, the true symbol of freedom, the real deserving, he believed.

His deep and strong belief that "education and science when properly applied could solve most of the problems" was known far and wide.

His Agricultural Extension Service was organized to bring rural California the latest truths in scientific as well as practical agriculture. Of all the programs which he fostered and promoted to aid California agriculture, the one closest to his heart was the 4-H Club movement—the development of rural boys and girls on California farms. His life's work the development of the California Agricultural Extension Service, was known as the best in the world.

As a lecturer and teacher he had no peer. From the platform he was cheered and applauded by friend and foe alike. His speeches were forceful, entertaining, and factual. His ability to simplify and analyze difficult subjects was an accomplishment that comes to few men. His honesty and foresight, his dignity and gentlemanly courteous manners, were admired by all who knew him.

He believed in hard work; that is, hard work well planned, which his own personal record bears out by the following quotation. "A task without a vision is drudgery. A vision without a task is a dream. But a task and vision together are joys unspeakable."

He often advised his Extension personnel that, "If you want to improve yourself, there are three ways to do so: (1) attend some great university, such as Cornell, Penn State, Iowa, or California; (2) surround yourself with people that know more than you do; and (3) travel. I don't pay you enough to travel, but you should do it anyway."

J. E. Tippett, assistant state director, flanked Crocheron throughout his brilliant career. Many strongly believe that "Tipp's" advice and counsel was highly responsible for the Chief's huge success.

If I were to propose a toast to him, I would say, "Here's to our courageous and faithful leader, an outstanding teacher and educator, a capable organizer, a champion of the rural people, a man the world around!"

Dempsey vs. Louis

Meeting the champ — Dr. Glen Albaugh (my son) and Jack Dempsey at Jack's Restaurant, New York City

This is an imaginary fight between Jack **Dempsey, the** "Manassa Mauler" of ring fame and Joe Lewis, the "brown bomber" of the squared circle. The scene is Reno, Nevada, "The biggest little city in the world," located on the banks of the snow-laden waters of the Truckee River.

Tex Rickard, the most colorful fight stager of all times, is the promoter. He has built a huge outdoor arena of a full 90,000 capacity under the very shadows of the rugged Sierra Nevada mountain range. Arthur Donovan, dean of arbitrators, is the referee. Jim Jeffries, the punchproof, man-killer exheavyweight of two score years ago, and Jack Johnson, whose golden smile and cagey ring work made him famous in fight history, are the judges.

It's July 4, 1926. Both fighters are in their prime and in perfect shape. Louis is 26 and is weighing 195 pounds of strong bone and muscle. Dempsey is 23 and his panther-like body tips the beam to 187 ½. It's a perfect night—balmy and summery. A cheering, angry, hungry and milling crowd from all corners of the globe has filled Tex's huge stadium "plumb to the rafters". The winner of this unique ring battle will receive a million dollars in cold cash, while the loser will get only a slice of the movie rights.

The two great idols are entering the ring at the same time. They are getting a tremendous ovation, which echoes throughout the length of this silver state of Nevada. Dempsey is wearing his winning black trunks. He appears in the pink of condition. His heavy-muscled, well-built body is deeply tanned from the rays of the desert sun, giving his body a burnished, bronze hue, and he resembles the red-skinned Indian. He has a scowl on his prominent, battle-scarred brow, and a two-day growth of black, wiry beard covers his face. He appears as nervous and nimble as a treed cat. Louis has on his famous lucky purple trunks and appears stronger and huskier than his popular opponent. His poker face is as expressionless as a cake of ice and he seems to be just as cold and calm.

The betting is heavy and it's even money. There are plenty of greenbacks offered, but no takers that the fight won't go the route—15 rounds of gruesome, gruelling fighting. The blood-thirsty crowd underneath the starry mountain sky know full well that both men are dangerous every minute they are on their feet. The shrewd and crafty Jack Kerns stands in Dempsey's corner whispering words of wisdom into Jack's ear. In Joe's corner is the famed and renowned Jack Blackburn, who is leaning over the ropes directing Louis in the final act of this great ring drama.

Donovan gives them the usual instructions and the bell for the first round rings out, puncturing the mountain air like a rifle shot. The battle is on! Both men are cautious. The crowd is tense. Dempsey has been instructed to be careful. Louis needs no coaching! Blackburn has schooled him well.

After sparring for a few seconds, Dempsey throws a vicious left hook that lands under Joes right ear. It spins the Negro half around and tears his ear partly loose from his curly, shining head. Jack misses a right to the chin and Louis catches him with a cutting left over the right eye, which starts the blood flowing, partially obstructing his vision. Kerns is anxious for his fighter and yells to Jack, "Box!"

Louis is the master at these long-range tactics, jabbing and blocking as Jack moves in close. Some savage in-fighting takes place and both men give and take plenty of punishment at close range. Dempsey throws a straight left that lands in Joe's mid-section. The colored man's mouth flies open and he loses his mouthpiece. The din and noise from the crowd is so loud that neither fighter hears the bell. A second after the bell, Dempsey lands a right upper-cut which drops Joe to the canvas, writhing in pain. They are dragging the "brown bomber" to his corner, his brain numbed, and the poker expression on his face has gone. He has been badly hurt for the first time in his career, but he will recuperate rapidly under expert hands. Donovan warns Jack about hitting after the bell.

At the clang of the bell for the second frame, Jack, in panther-like style, springs across the ring and meets Joe almost in his corner, tearing in for the kill. Lefts and rights thud against the body and head of Joe Louis with all the fury and speed of a Henry Armstrong. The "killer" of the ring looks good. Louis rolls beautifully with the punches, grabs and holds on, only to be pried apart by Donovan. He weathers the storm and fights back with the courage and skill of a wounded wild animal at bay. Joe throws a sharp, cutting left to Jack's head bringing forth a new flow of blood. As Jack starts to lead, Joe rips a right to the jaw that sends his opponent to the mat. Kerns yells for Jack to take the count of 9, but in true Dempsey style, he is up at 2, going after Louis, who bicycles across the ring. Blood drips from Jack's brow. He looks anxious and hurt—a gory sight. Louis shuffles out, feints Jack off balance, and punishes him with rights and lefts to the head. They go into a clinch. At the bell, Louis drops Jack again with a left hook to the jaw and the crowd goes wild. It's Louis round by a wide margin. Kerns is worried. Black-burn smiles.

Round three and the man from the deep south shuffles out flat-footed. Jack is up on his toes, bobbing and weaving in his famous crouch and as full of fight as ever. Louis shoots lefts and opens up the cut on Jack's eye. They go into a clinch and Demp-sey jerks away, throwing Joe into the ropes savagely. The referee steps between them; Jack pushes Donovan aside and they both come in fighting hard and dangerously. Jack lands a terrific left over Joe's heart, which makes his knees sag, and Louis hooks a wicked right to the chin. Both fighters kiss the canvas. The referee is confused, but finally starts the count. Jack is up, as usual, at 3, but Joe is smart. He takes his time and gets up at 9, somewhat groggy, where he meets a ferocious Dempsey, who charges in only to be out-boxed and out-maneuvered by the colored man. The round is even. Blackburn tells his methodical fighter to wear his opponent down with cutting, twisting punches to the body and face. Dempsey's instructions are to knock the colored man out soon; the next round.

The fourth round—Dempsey moves out of his corner in a low and weaving fashion and goes into a half-crouch. He hits Joe several blows in the mid-section which bring pain to the colored man's face, showing that these blows are taking their toll. Blood trickles from the corners of Joe's mouth, indicating that he might be hurt internally. Joe tries to box, but Jack keeps on top of him. He knows his best defense is a rugged and aggressive offense. Jack rains body blows on the Negro. These are hard and difficult for any fighter to absorb. Louis has slowed up. He backs away, but Jack keeps coming forward— bobbing, weaving, stabbing, hooking, jolting, and throwing blows from all angles. He is the master at the in-fighting. Louis grabs his midsection and appeals to the referee that he has been hit low. Blackburn jumps into the ring. There is much confusion. The fight is stopped and a physician is called to examine Joe. He pronounces the blow legal and Donovan orders that the fight continue, but in so doing warns Jack to watch his blows. Blackburn has told Louis to coast this round, to box Dempsey and to keep his eyes cut and bleeding, thinking that these tactics will slow up the man from Colorado. Joe carries out his instructions well, but it's Dempsey's round and he appears to have regained his strength.

At the beginning of the fifth round, Louis comes out punching wickedly. Jack meets him in the center of the ring, where they stand toe to toe and slug with all their might and skill. Joe hooks a devastating right to Jack's jaw and he falls forward in a clinch and holds on precariously. The referee is unable to part them. Joe finally jerks loose, spinning Jack around, and in so doing pulls his right glove half-way off. The fight is stopped to replace the glove. This saves Jack for he is badly hurt and groggy. Louis continues to circle Dempsey and with short, accurate jabs he cuts Jack's bloody and swollen face to ribbons. Jack tries to get in close to work on Joe's "bread-basket", but Louis holds him off with his superior boxing ability. It's Joe's round, and the end of the fight seems near.

In the sixth round Joe meets his opponent with confidence for he seems to smell victory. Jack's eyes are partially closed, but his fighting heart and unequalled courage carry him always forward, never backward. Joe starts a long left for Jack's cut eye. At the same instant Dempsey sees an opening and shoots a murderous right, which catches Joe flush on the button. He slumps forward and his knees buckle, and Dempsey hooks a left to the jaw. Joe falls forward on his face, a victim of the mauler's famed one-two. The referee counts, and Louis, a most colorful, clean and splendid fighter is counted out. Jack Dempsey's powerful punch, coupled with his aggressive, killer style, and that great will to win, proved too much for the "brown bomber" from the cotton fields of Alabama.

Thus ends an imaginary contest between two of the greatest fighters of all time. One fought a planned, organized battle; the other batted by instinct and opportunity. You can't beat nature's ways.

The pride of Long Valley — Kenneth, Wes and Harold Eade, San Lucas, Calif.

Cow Country's Champion

Many reasons can be bunched up in the old tally book as to why the West is different, separate and apart from the rest of the great wide world. The very topography of that rangeland — including the mountains, streams, rivers, forests and plains of that portion of the country that mothered the buffalo, coyote, ground squirrel and the rattlesnake — typifies some of its uniqueness. Then, of course, you have the smell of sage, the famous barbed wire, the windmill, the cow pony, the square dance.

But above all of these is the cattleman himself. Each community of the West has its famous character, and he usually adds more color and glamour to this land of the sinking sun than do all the other factors combined. His fame, courteous manner, his real hospitality, his genuine friendliness, his very speech or lingo, his ways of entertaining, and his clever and descriptive sayings are unlike those that are found elsewhere on the globe.

Monterey County has its share of these Sons of the West — the men called "the salt of the earth" and the "diamonds in the rough." Outstanding among these is none other than W. C. "Wes" Eade, pride and joy of the cattle country of San Lucas.

Wes' pedigree, according to him, is probably not as long nor as blueblooded as some that might be found in *Who's Who In America*, but he is very proud of his old English ancestry. His family tree indicates that his grandfather came from Pensance, England, and his grandfather hailed from Durham County of the same country. They migrated to America at an early date and settled in Illinois.

His father was a miner and during the Gold Rush Days of '49 when the yellow dirt stampeded the pioneer, he joined one of the covered wagon trains and crossed the plains with his parents. During the trek, Wes's grandfather contracted the dreaded disease, cholera, and was buried by his son on the lone bleak prairie.

In spite of this great sad disappointment to a 16-year-old-boy, Wes' father continued on and reached the "sunset land" where he worked in the mines for several years, accumulating considerable wealth. The gold dust that he panned from the creeks in the Golden State was put into a belt and sewed around his waist and carried back to the middle west via the Isthmus of Panama. He married shortly, later, returning to California in 1884. Thirteen children were born to this union. Of these, Wes became the outstanding cattleman of the group, accumulating over 22,000 acres of land and 3,000 head of cattle.

As we sat on a green, grass-covered hill in Long Valley discussing his life story, Wes said, "This is as good a cattle country as you can find outdoors. The bur clover and filaree that grow here are very rich feed. Some years it becomes so abundant and high in quality that cattle die of bloat. It's even good country after it's been sandpapered off by overgrazing because the cattle lick up the rich bur clover burs and stay fat.

When Wes was 16 years old he started punching cows for the famous Henry Miller, cattle king of California, Oregon and Nevada, who operated during the "Roaring Eighties," the "Gay Nineties," and a decade that passed the turn of the century. For 10 years, he served in various capacities under this shrewd cattle operator, an expert cattle judge, a clever, crafty dealer.

During the wet cycles Miller would pile up great stacks of hay and straw, and then when "Old Man Drought" came — which happened quite often — he would either sell this feed at a high price or buy the less fortunate operator's cattle for a song. This practice made him wealthy.

One day Wes met Henry Miller at San Lucas and took him to the Peach Tree Ranch in a buggy. As they reached San Lorenzo Creek, Miller asked if any cattle had been dying from anthrax. Wes replied, "No." In so doing, he was protecting the foreman of the ranch. There was a steer lying close to the road that had died from this disease and his carcass had been dragged across the road and dumped into the creek bed. Miller spied this well-marked trail and immediately got out of the buggy and went over to inspect the river bed. Here he found some 40 head of cattle that had died from this dreaded disease and had not been skinned. This was the last straw. He took off his new black hat, threw it on the ground, jumped on it with both feet and said, "Young man, you lied to me! A liar is worse than a thief. You can watch a thief but you can't watch a liar."

Wes became an expert cowboy while in Miller's employ, and the saying goes in the San Lucas Country that he could ride anything that wore hair.

Furthermore, he was a real scrapper and in his heyday his friends say he could lick any man that walked!!! To quote Wes, "I didn't go touring around looking for a fight, but when one of these hombres got on the prod, I usually could accommodate him."

Even back only a few years ago, Wes demonstrated that he was still king of his community when he separated two burly barroom fighters at Hank's old saloon. This incident took place during a chivaree held for Bill Casey, a neighboring cowman of Long Valley. A group of celebrants entered this establishment for some "light liquid" refreshments. George Mee of the Peach Tree Ranch and the late Bert Sooey, of Cow Palace fame, were flanking the hero of this story as he entered this noisy, smokey hall. As the fight progressed, it became one-sided. Wes, a stickler for fair play, immediately stepped in, despite his 60 some years, and tore the two dangerous fighters apart and told them in no uncertain terms to leave the community. Both bullies thanked Wes and pulled out for parts unknown.

The first money that Wes borrowed, $250, was from Henry Miller. "I paid 1 percent interest compounded per month on this sum of money," says Wes, "and I learned considerable about financing from this baron of the west, who was a champion when it came to picking clients to whom to loan money."

About 1900, Wes married Miss Bessie Bray. The wedding took place at the old Los Palmas Ranch near Salinas, now owned by Violini Brothers. Their family consisted of 3 girls and 3 boys, all of whom reside in and around King City and San Lucas, except John who passed away in 1928.

Wes Eade's operations have been unique in that he has been a buyer and a seller during his entire career. He never built up a good cow and calf herd because there was too much risk in having to dispose of these high-priced cattle during a time of drought. He used as his slogan during those years "Buy cheap and sell high." It sounds easy, but it was hard to do.

It takes natural instinct and ability to sense a good deal and to carry it through to successful completion. People, like Wes, are born with this ability. Very few acquire it.

During the past few years Wes has been running Braham crossbred cattle. He claims that they're the best of any. "They're cheap cattle, it costs less to run them, and even though one doesn't receive as much per pound there are more chips left at the end of the season. These cattle will go miles for a drink and live on short grass, and still come out looking slick and fat."

It has been said that Wes Eade has bought and sold more cattle than most people in this area. Most of his purchases were made in the southwest, including Arizona, Texas, New Mexico, and south of the border in old Mexico.

In carrying on these operations Wes wrote very few letters. Most of his communications were carried on by telephone and telegraph. The reading of government bulletins, government market reports, magazines and other material of that sort was not incorporated in his business activities. On the other hand, he got timely and accurate information on the cattle business from reliable acquaintances of big-time cattle interests.

Livestock meetings did not attract this successful cattleman's interest. In fact, when asked about this, he stated, "I've attended only two meetings of this sort during the last 20 years." One was a corn-hog meeting in King City, back in 1934. The other one was when he was invited as a guest at a meeting arranged by Nelson Crow of the Western Livestock Journal on one of the tours through this area. "I recall this meeting very well," Wes went on to say, "because of a story about a glass-eyed banker that was told at the meeting. It seems as though this story originated during tough times in the cow business. A cattleman was talking to his banker regarding borrowing more money. The banker agreed to give him this loan if he could tell which of his eyes was glass. The cattleman looked the banker over carefully and finally said it was the left eye. The financier was surprised that he was right and asked the cattleman how he knew. This he replied, "I thought I could see a little human kindness in that left eye."

Although Wes did not avail himself of the educational and scientific information that is available on the cattle industry today, it is his opinion that young men engaged in the business should take advantage of these reliable facts. In fact, his sons have followed their dad's advice in this regard and are using new scientific methods.

Wes is very proud of his two sons. "One of the things I tried to do," claims Wes, "was to train them so that they would be better operators than I. Either of them can crawl off a horse, pull off his spurs and handle himself like a top hand at most any meeting."

Although he didn't say so, the raising and training of 3 girls and 3 boys to be outstanding, successful citizens was the most important job Wes and Mrs. Eade have accomplished. This, one could read between the lines.

"Who was the best cowboy you ever had work for you," was the question asked of this colorful individual. Immediately he said, "Shorty Williamson. I've had a lot of good cowboys work for me in my day, but Shorty was the all-around best. He could ride a tough horse, knew how to handle cattle, and best of all, was a shrewd buyer and seller. He carried my checkbook for years and bought cattle for me in many parts of the country. He's as honest as the day is long. Our three boys grew up with Shorty and I'm sure proud they did."

As the conversation drifted to cow horses, Wes said, "They're like women and dogs! You find only one or two good ones in a lifetime. Usually these good horses are well bred with some hot blood in them. The Tresconys own good ones. Most of the fellows who broke these horses were Spanish or Mexican and to show you how well reined they were in those early days, I'll tell you the story told by Vincente Feliz, an outstanding cowboy with a gift for imaginary stories who worked many years for me.

"Vincente was riding one of these well-reined horses when he came upon an old mossy-horned steer up in the high peaks of the Pancho Rico country. As he was closing in to rope this steer, a wide gulch loomed in the foreground. The steer successfully negotiated the gulch, but as the horse started across, Vincente saw that he could not make the jump. Half way across the gulch, while still in mid-air, he turned the horse around and took him back to the side where he started the jump."

Wes has been prominent in rodeos, having been one of the first directors of the California Rodeo at Salinas. He has acted as judge of cow horses at many of the western performances. He has also been one of the strongest supporters of and bidders in, junior fat stock sales throughout Monterey County, helping the boys and girls get full value for their livestock projects.

"How many times have you gone broke since you've been in the cattle business?" I asked. This great character scratched his head and said, "I've never been clear down and out yet, but back in 1934 and '35 the bankers were sure nippin' close on my heels. With a little luck and some fast talk, I pulled through."

"Do any of these cattlemen who go broke ever recover?" was another question asked him. To this he answered, "Very few of them make that comeback trail. I can think of more men who never made the grade back than those who did. It's wounded pride that usually keeps them down."

"Severe droughts and fluctuation in prices of cattle are the two main things that break people engaged in this business. Of the two, drought is the hardest one with which to contend because it cannot be predicted. If you watch your p's and q's and are careful on your marketings, fluctuation of prices many times can be averted.

"Anyone can be a cattleman when the filaree and bur clover are a foot high and prices are good, but when it fails to rain and the markets drop, that's when the boys are separated from the men in this old fascinating business.

One neighbor said, "Wes Eade is the only cattleman I know who came up the hard way, made a success, and is living his life today just the way he wants to."

A few years ago Wes was chosen as a member of the Cowboy Hall of Fame. His portrait hangs in this shrine in Oklahoma City.

As Henry Miller sat in his twilight of life figuratively looking over his million acres of land and million head of cattle, he was sad and depressed. All of this wealth had been accumulated, yet he had no son to carry on and to perpetuate the HH holdings. Unlike the famous Miller, it is generally agreed that when Wes "goes over the Great Divide" to that new range where the grass never fails and the streams run bankful that his boots here will be filled by his two capable sons, Kenneth and Harold.

Bert Sooy of Cow Palace fame.

He Rides the "Point"

Promoting beef — Carl Garrison, Jake Schneider, Gov. Goodwin Knight, Sloughouse, Calif.

Carl L. Garrison, Manager of Porter Estate Company, has, in addition to ramrodding this Company's far-flung cattle interests and diversified farming activities in California and Nevada, became owner of one ranch, a part of the original El Solyo near Tracy, a general partner of the Atherton Cattle Company and president and shareholder of a large diversified ranch corporation in Southern Monterey County.

How did he do it? Not with a long, accurate rope, fast horse and a running iron as in the days of the early west, but by hard work and a lot of luck. Those who know this keen, hard working cattleman are aware that he clawed his way to the top by using sound, fundamental business principles coupled with scientific "know how.' There is a saying that the harder you work, the luckier you are. Carl firmly believes in this cardinal trait. In other words, he was reared during an era when hard work was considered dignified and holy.

This outstanding leader in agriculture was born in Bieber, Lassen County, California and lived on a ranch all of his life prior to going away to college. Here he learned at an early age to care for livestock and till the blessed earth. He was an active 4-H Club member at an early age. He raised a champion hog which feat entitled him to attend a 4-H Club convention at Davis in the early 20's.

In 1929, as a Future Farmer High School Senior, he won the State of California Dairy Council's butter essay contest. This is when members of the Dairy Council were influential in Carl's decision to enroll in the University of California at Davis in the fall of 1929 to study Animal Husbandry.

The effects of the stock market crash triggered the great depression and money was scarce and tight. Carl obtained jobs at the beef and dairy barns and was lucky to occupy an 8x10 room in the goat barn. He also took care of the small animal (rat and mice) colony in order to secure money to put himself through college. He graduated in 1933 with a B.S. Degree in Animal Science with flying colors. While a student at the University of California at Davis, he was active in many campus activities: Alpha Gamma Rho Fraternity, Junior Class president, Rally Committee chairman, Scabbard and Blade and a member of the Student Executive Committee. He also served as a member of the Annual Picnic Day Committee on two or three occasions

Upon graduation from Davis, he received a degree in secondary education in the field of vocational agriculture. After one year as head of the Agriculture Department in the Red Bluff High School, he was appointed assistant farm advisor in San Joaquin County. Here he served with distinction for 5 years assisting with the 4-H Club beef cattle and swine programs. He was also in charge of the field crop programs in the County.

In 1936 while heading up the 4-H Club activities at California State Fair, he met and later married a city-raised girl, Jeanne Hubbard. Jeanne adapted readily to western ranch life and became an ardent collector of barbed wire. The Garrisons have four daughters and all have followed in their father's footsteps by receiving their formal education at U.C.D.

This northern Californian native was called to active duty with the U.S Air Force early in 1941 where he served for five years and returned home with the rank of Colonel in the Air Force Reserve.

Following the war, he was named the first permanent Manager of the Cow Palace and in 1951 left there to become associated with the Porter Estate Company as general manager. During the next 20 years his work and activities for the betterment of the cattle business and University of California were so extensive and important that they would "choke a horse."

CATTLE INDUSTRY:

Director of California Cattlemen's Association since 1953— 18 years.

First Chairman California Beef Industry Council — 1954

Chairman California Beef Council — 1959-60.
   Former Vice President and Director of National Beef Council.

Former Chairman Agriculture Committee, San Francisco Chamber of Commerce — 2 years.

Member of the First California Livestock Symposium Steering Committee — 1969;
   Chairman, Agitator Panel — 1970.

Grand National Junior Livestock Exposition Advisory Committee — 20 years; Chairman — several years

Chairman or Co-Chairman Grand National and Junior Grand National Sales Committee — 16 years.

Former President Californians for Fairs.

Director and Trail Captain, Woodside Trail Club.

Former Director and Secretary, California Reined Cow Horse Association.

Named Honorary Director California Rodeo, Salinas — 1963.

Former Director, International Rodeo Association.

An excellent livestock judge, Carl has graded bulls at Red Bluff, Cedarville and Cal Poly. He has also acted as an official judge at the Cow Palace and many county and district fairs.

Always willing and ready to test new improved practices, the Porter Estate Company has co-operated closely with farm advisors on various field trials with field crops and livestock. Carl has appeared as feature speaker at numerous University Sponsored educational meetings. His hobbies are hunting, riding, roping and amateur photography:

HIS UNIVERSITY OF CALIFORNIA SERVICES INCLUDED:

Member of University of California President's First Advisory Committee for College of Agriculture.

President California Aggie Alumni Association — 2 years 1938-1939; now serving as First Vice President and member of Executive Committee.

Member California Aggie Alumni Foundation Board of Directors.

Served as Chairman California Aggie Alumni Committee for the Future.

Former Member of an Alumni Advisory Committee on Curriculum, UCD.

Chairman, California Agricultural Council Advisory Committee to the Animal Husbandry Department, UCD.

Besides taking part in all these activities, he has successfully managed the Porter Estate Company's agricultural interests and and has become owner, part owner and/or partner in three ranching enterprises. Leaders of the industry have recognized Carl's leadership and organization ability and have bestowed upon him the following awards and honors:

California Livestock Man of the Year — 1963.

Recipient of Bank of America — Grand National Junior Livestock Exposition Award — 1969.

Honorary Degree of State Farmer — 1948.

Guest of Honor — Golden Hoof Club's Little International — 1950.

This livestock man of the year is also an active member of the following organizations:

Bohemian Club — San Francisco

Commonwealth Club — San Francisco

California Wood Growers Association

California Cattle Feeders Association

This generous, unselfish humanitarian is not only a successful cattleman, but a leader in the industry and always is championing the cause for those engaged in research and education. Only in America where the free enterprise system prevails could such success be accomplished. Yes, Carl Garrison has the strength of character to rise above weariness and the bold courage to walk over fear. Impeccably dressed for any occasion, he rides the "point" with the air and know-how of a real champion.

Champion of Champions

Riding high, wide and handsome — Jesse Stahl on Glass Eye.
Courtesy Dr. E. J. Leach, Salinas, Calif.

It was an afternoon in July, 1940. The range grasses have withered and the hills have turned brown. The cattle shipping is all done. The Cowpokes who inhabit the sage brush, the poison oak and bunch grass country are drifting into Salinas, the county seat and great cow town of old and colorful Monterey County, California. Here they are gathered to vie for honors at the California Rodeo, the best of its kind in the land. They will contest to see if they deserve the right to wear the jingling spur, the high-heeled boots, and the 10-gallon hat.

The old town is decorated in bright and brilliant colors, depicting the carefree Spanish days of yesteryears. The old western spirit of the pioneer days is in the air.

Sport loving range folk from far and wide have gathered to witness this unique wild west show and to reminisce of days gone by and discuss livestock and range conditions of parts back home.

Hundreds of big powerful whitefaced bulls with dusty backs, together with long-horned Mexican steers, thin of flank and with the speed of a race horse, have been assembled to offer thrills for this "hungry" and anxious crowd.

From the parched lands of Arizona; from the lava beds of Modoc; from the sage brush plains of Nevada; and the bunch grass mountains of Oregon have come some of the toughest of bucking broncs.

Everything humanly possible has been done to make this rodeo click. It is a champion show; the contestants who win at Salinas will be crowned champion cowboy of the whole wide world. The first 3 days of this thrilling show are over; it is Sunday and the finals of all events are at hand; competition is keen and an undercurrent of tenseness lingers throughout the dusty sun-kist air.

All eyes are on the bucking shoots. Riders in the bronc riding contest have been eliminated except four—but what a quartet. They are famous—renowned—great in all departments of rodeo sports. On the imaginary program they are listed as follows:

Perry Ivory—that handsome, curly-haired, tall, wiry puncher from the Modoc country.

Pete Knight—that natural, easy and well-balanced twister from deep in the mountains of Idaho.

Jess Stahl—the strong, rough and ready colored cowboy from the cotton fields of Texas.

And last but not least is the daredevil, loose-riding youth from the bad lands of South Dakota, Casey Tibbs.

They have drawn their mounts and Abe Lefton, the premier rodeo announcer of all times, has just told the audience that Ivory will ride The Crying Jew, a big feather-legged, strong-bucker, fresh off the Gabilan range. Knight has drawn Tumbleweed—the high-kicking crooked bronc from the sage brush flats of the silver state, Nevada. Glasseye, the bald-faced spectacular bucker from the Sierra mountains will be forked in this thrilling contest by Jess Stahl. Joker, that ridge-running roan from the rim rocks of old Arizona will be contested by Tibbs.

The judges are at their posts, all veterans of this show judging business. They are: Shorty Williamson of King City; Elton Hebbron and Grover Tholcke of Salinas.

Ivory is the first to ride. His mount is difficult to saddle. The "Jew" has tried to climb out of the chute and has thrown himself but finally has the rigging strapped on. Tholcke instructs Ivory to climb aboard and come out scratching. Perry winks at one of the judges—pulls his hat down tight—looks at his spurs and slowly and carefully but with an air of determination slides down the middle of one of the greatest bucking broncs that ever wore a saddle. The "Jew" looks back and is anxious to be given daylight. Perry takes a deep seat in that old association saddle and says, "Let me have him." Crying Jew bursts out of the chute like a lion out of a cage and makes a tremendous jump high into the air, at the same time kicking very high behind.

Ivory, with his spurs in his mount's shoulders, leans way back and rides his stirrups heavily. He knows that if he can stick the first three jumps his bronc has been mastered. The jumps are now faster—not so high or long— but he continues to kick so high that he almost falls over forward. Ivory pays no attention to the judges or to the audience but continues to spur the big bay in the shoulders. The fifth jump is past and Perry rakes his horse high behind. It is a master ride and the crowd lets the judges know their approval.

Stahl is the next rider. His horse, Glasseye, is saddled. One of his helpers pulls the flank rigging up tight and Jess slips down on his mount, seemingly unconcerned, laughing, talking to the cowboys on the chute. Ice water must flow through this colored boy's veins. Will Rogers, the humorist, columnist, and cowboy actor leans over the chute and tells Jess that if he is to win this contest he must make a clean but spectacular exhibition of horsemanship. Glasseye makes two big jumps forward and rears high and literally walks and bucks on his two hind feet. Stahl pays no attention to his mount but keeps spurring and looking over his shoulders, smiling toward the grandstand and saying in that southern drawl, "Look close, mista judges, and see if I'm spurrin' that old hoss in both shouldahs." It is a showy crowd-pleasing ride but the judges mark their cards and order Knight out on Tumbleweed.

This great natural rider comes out on the big brown horse riding by sheer balance. For the first five jumps rider and horse are synchronized as one. On the sixth jump, Tumbleweed partly falls to his knees. Knight is loosened up, he is off balance. The bronc senses his rider's difficulty and starts spinning and at the same time kicking high behind. Knight grabs for leather but is too late. Tumbleweed is out from under him and he kisses old Mother Earth—another victim for this vicious bronc from old Nevada.

The 19-year-old kid, Casey Tibbs, is pale and nervous with only two years of experience behind him. He pulls on his chaps and slides down onto the summit of the crookedest and fastest bronc that ever saw daylight in Salinas. As the chute gate opens, Casey's spurs are right behind the ears of this ridge-running roan. On the first jump he rakes his horse plumb to the cantle board of his saddle. He is riding very loose. The horse is swapping ends in the air. Casey continues to spur and kick his horse wherever he can touch him, determined to ride him through.

The crowd is going wild. They like this kid from South Dakota. Tibbs is bucked off—no, the horse catches him and he is back on spurring again. He is partially off again but the horse again bucks under him and he rides on to the finish. It is a careless slam bang ride that only a youth could make on a dangerous rough bronc. The crowd likes it but the judges thought Tibbs was lucky and after some consideration they gave the nod to Ivory. Tibbs was 2nd, and Stahl 3rd. Thus ended an imaginary bronc riding contest among four of the greatest cowboys that ever sat in a saddle. Ivory's consistent know how methods of riding tough horses in his easy, pleasing fashion proved too much for the other cowpokes in this contest. At his height it has been said by many that when the chips were down Ivory could ride any horse on the circuit the judges' way—the winning way.

The Great One

Tales of broncs — the author chats with Perry Ivory.

The year was 1919 when the boys in Khaki were straggling home from Flanders field and the tough Rhine country. President Woodrow Wilson was stumping the country on the merits of the League of Nations. Jack Dempsey, the Manassa Mauler, had knocked out the giant Jess Willard for the heavyweight championship of the world. George Herman Ruth known as "Babe" and "sultan of swat" was filling Yankee Stadium with his home-run ball.

In the rodeo sport, 1919 launched a distinguished career of a tall, wiry, curly-haired cowboy, Perry Ivory. It was autumn and the rodeo season at Madison Square was on. As Perry stepped off the train at New York's Penn Station dressed in boots and Stetson hat, he set his straw suitcase down and said aloud to himself, "This station is bigger than all of Alturas."

He was afraid, lonely, and worried, but down deep inside he had a burning desire to be a champion bronc rider. With all the western courage he possessed, Perry sidled up to a well-dressed stranger and said politely, "Sir, I am lost! Can you tell me how to find Madison Square Garden?"

Five days later this unknown cowboy from the Modoc country pocketed $1,500 third money. This was feat enough among rodeo's best, but what took the big city by storm, was the cowboy's age—Perry was 16! This was only the beginning of an outstanding rodeo career blasting through the Roaring 20's and Democratic 30's, known also as the "Golden Age of Sport."

Perry went on to win at all the major shows around the world, including those in the U.S., Canada, England and Australia. Many authorities on Wild West Shows maintain that Ivory's performance in the rodeo arena equalled Dempsey's accomplishments in the squared circle and paralleled those of Ruth on the baseball diamond. These same authorities are of the opinion that if the accomplishments of all great bronc riders were computerized, Ivory would emerge as the supreme champion of champions.

Ivory started his outstanding career as a fuzzy-faced youth at the tender age of 14 entering a wild horse race at a rodeo in Reno, Nevada. He made his debut as a bronc rider at the age of 15 at the Lakeview Roundup in Oregon.

He was born in Dorris, Siskiyou County, California, just past the turn of the century. When 6 years old, his father died and he and his mother moved to Sparks, Nevada. Perry spent most of his summers on his Uncle Ed's ranch near Alturas. Ed Ivory was an expert horseman, an excellent cattleman, and he taught Perry the fine points of handling livestock, especially riding bucking horses.

In 1934, after a long sea voyage, Perry and other western contestants arrived in Melbourne, Australia, where they competed in a scheduled 6-day rodeo—the first Wild West Show to be staged in that "down under" country. At the end of 5 days, Perry was leading in bronc riding; then because of rain the show was cancelled. He observed that the horses in Australia were smaller and carried more Thoroughbred breeding than those in the U.S.A. They were spectacular, showy buckers, but not too tough to ride. He liked the people in Australia because they were friendly and courteous.

The biggest show in which he ever competed was in London, England, where over 150,000 people attended. He won third money in bronc riding and pocketed $3,500. That was in 1934, in the days when a dollar was worth a dollar.

"What was the hardest horse you ever rode, Perry?" This top bronc rider scratched his head and thought deeply for a few seconds then said, "I think it was the 'Crying Jew.' The reason it was so difficult to stay aboard this horse," he continued, "was because he was big, fast, kicked real high behind and he was a head tosser. He would throw his head up and wink at you."

"How about the 'McArthur Special'? Wasn't he pretty tough? "Yes," said Perry, "He was one of the good ones—big and strong. But there were others like the 'Jew' that were tougher. The 'Special' bucked me off a second after the whistle sounded at the Chester Rodeo, and I landed in the grandstand." One of the spectators said, 'Young man, why did you jump off that horse?' I answered, "I wanted to make this show a little wilder than some of the others."

Perry recalled, "Roderick McArthur sold the 'Special' and he went into a bucking string. After a few months on the circuit, the 'Special' died, bucked so hard he broke a blood vessel and died with his saddle on."

"Charles Stover ramrodded the Chester Show and he was one of the finest men I ever met." The same goes for Roderick. McArthur," Perry said.

"Old Duster was also one of the greatest," continued Perry. "He bucked everybody off. Next to Midnight, he was the greatest bucking horse that ever lived. He bucked Pete Knight off and killed him. He was raised in Susanville, originally owned by Peter Welch. Kids used to ride him to school. They got to cracking walnuts on the saddle horn and he pitched them off. This made him a great bucking horse." "Five Minutes to Midnight" was also one of the greatest bucking horses. He was a small horse but a terrific bucker; bucked me off!"

When asked about some of the best bronc riders that he met during his career, Perry answered, "Bob Askin, Pete Knight, Jerry Ambler, and Earl Thode were some of the best. They could not only ride top horses and qualify, but they were crowd pleasers as well. Compared to these young fellows, there are very few of the present-day bronc riders that could carry Pete Knight's bucking rein. Most of them are better educated and they train more scientifically than we did. They don't carouse around and drink like the old-timers. It's more of a profession with them."

"Take Casey Tibbs. He won a lot of money and must go down in history as one of the very best. He was one of the top riders during his generation. This boy from the badlands of the Dakotas, like all of us, had trouble with big, tough head-throwing horses."

'How are you supposed to ride these head-slingers, Perry?"

He answered, "It has to be a loose rein and you have to handle it something like you would when fishing for trout with a fly rod; otherwise, they will pull you right over their heads."

"I rode all the top horses on the circuits during the 1920's and 30's continued Ivory, "except one, and that was Midnight. I never did draw him. That big, strong, black, feather-legged northern horse was almost impossible for a human to ride when he was at his best. He bucked crooked; kicked high, threw his head; and sometimes when he was up in the air, he would shake himself like a dog coming out of water."

"Tell me something about the different kinds of bucking broncs, Perry." "Well, in order to have a rodeo you must have bucking horses," said Perry. "There are many types of these animals, and any cowboy that signs on the dotted line usually has to earn his prize money by riding a trained, vicious bucker.

"The spinner is probably one of the most unusual types of bucking horses that performs. He comes out of the chute and bucks over a small area, usually in a circle. The cowboy who rides him must have a very good sense of balance and at the same time must be able to follow the rules of the rodeo. If this type of horse is fast enough, he generally unloads the cowboy, who becomes dizzy and unfamiliar with his directions and surroundings.

The straight-away bucker is one that most people think is easy to ride. In some instances that is true. But one of the toughest bucking horses to ever see daylight at a rodeo was Scar Face and he was a straight-away bucker. The reason he was hard to ride is because he was big and strong, hit the ground hard, and kicked very high behind. There are only a few cowboys able to ride this type of horse. Usually about the second time one of these animals kicks high behind, the cantle catches the cowboy in the seat of the pants, and overboard he goes, looking for Mother Earth.

The head swinger is another difficult horse to master. Two outstanding horses that had this peculiar characteristic were Headlight and Nevada Kid. These horses usually unbalanced their rider either by jerking the rein loose or by pulling the cowboy over their head. The swinging of the head makes the balance of the cowboy uncertain and this horse is a tough one to stay aboard.

Then we have the crooked bucker—one who goes up in the air looking at the grandstand and comes down looking at the chutes. Pretty Socks is a horse of this type; and when he is fast, he is mightly hard to do anything with.

Another type is the runaway. This horse usually bolts from the chute, running at full speed for 30 or 40 yards. He then ducks his head and starts to unwind. Usually his first or second jump does the trick.

Then we have the sulker. This horse won't come out of the chute until he is ready. Usually when he is ready the cowboy is not, and it is a short ride.

Every cowboy rides his horse a little differently. We have the tight rider and the loose rider—the man who rides with sheer strength, and the man who rides from a sense of balance. Usually the loose rider depends more on his sense of balance, guesses what the horse is going to do next, and makes the best ride.

The late Pete Knight, one of the greatest loose riders the world has ever known, rode from balance. He seemed to be very relaxed and moved with the horse at every jump. Casey Tibbs and Pat Woods are two more examples of loose riders. I was also a loose rider, rode my stirrups heavily.

One of the greatest tight riders that rodeo circuit has ever known was probably Clay Carr of Visalia, California."

It was Perry's opinion that bucking horses are not as tough now as they used to be. They are breeding the wildness and orneriness out of horses as compared to the old days.

"Were there any Negro bronc riders during your career, Perry?" "Yes," he replied, "Jess Stahl, and he was one of the best. He was friendly, humorous, and everybody liked him. He was more or less a clown bronc rider. He would ride bulls backwards and ride horses double—he would jump on back of a bronc that another cowboy was riding. Jesse was the only cowboy I ever knew who could ride a tough bronc and not look at his horse—he was always watching the grandstand or judges and smiling. He had gold teeth and they used to call it the 'Golden Stahl Smile."

How much money did you win during your rodeo years? Perry answered by saying, "I didn't keep track, but it must have been between 2 and 3 hundred thousand dollars." Considering inflation, this would be between 4 and 5 hundred thousand dollars today."

"Did you ever get injured rodeoing?"

"I was pretty lucky," he stated. "I was never badly hurt riding on the circuit. I had my right knee broken three times. If it weren't for that, I could still ride a tough horse at 65 years of age. The most spectacular injury I received was at Salinas. That was back in the middle 30's. I was riding broncs, bulls and bulldogging steers. It was the second day of a four-day show. I was leading in all three events. As I finished dogging, and started across the arena, a Mexican longhorn took after me. In order to protect me, Charles Magenti, that all-around twister from the

Gilroy country, rode between me and the steer, but as he cut in his horse stepped on my left ankle and broke my foot. They took me to the hospital and put my foot in a cast. I went back and competed in these three events for the next two days and won first money in all three, giving me a grand sum of $2,000 in cash, a fine saddle and a gold watch. The last bronc I rode the final day was named Tumbleweed. Very few bronc riders rode him with two good feet, let alone one in a cast. This incident was publicized in the San Francisco Examiner under the 'Believe it or Not' column. It goes to show that the only way to kill a cowboy is to cut his head off and hide it.

I am glad I spent over two decades on the rodeo circuit. Rodeoing was satisfying and rewarding to me. One of the greatest thrills in my life was riding a tough horse the contest way. By this I mean you not only had to qualify—follow all the rules—but please the crowd as well. It's like any other type of show business—electrify the audience. You must be a showman, having a pleasing personality, coupled with that rare and intangible trait called 'color.' Dempsey had it, so did Ruth. They were the best in their field and both were crowd pleasers."

"Perry, you had it too."

Perry went on, "You also had to look good even when you were a loser. Dempsey looked good losing to Tunney on the long count. The crowd was for me when McArthur Special bucked me into the grandstand at Chester.

If I had my life to live over again, I would probably follow the rodeos. Besides riding broncs, I would develop and perfect my roping. Making a loop do what you want it to do is a science as well as an art. You can last longer at roping than riding and it's not so dangerous. This sport pays big money now, but was not too attractive during my professional days.

"Let's forget the past and have a drink. Perry, do you hunt or fish? What do you hunt?"

Perry answered, "Deer, quail, and pheasants. And I use my rope now and then to get down the steep banks where the fishing's always good."

As I sipped Ivory's firewater, I thought about the life of this handsome, curly, gray-haired, distinguished-looking bronc twister—his courage, ability, accomplishments, determination, great will to win, hardships, and his contributions to a sport that has kept the Old West alive. Yes, I thought to myself, cowboys like Perry Ivory are a breed of their own, possessing many of the high qualities such as toughness, fearlessness, intestinal fortitude, and determination—all cardinal traits that have made Americans heroes the world around.

Snake Eyes

It is Indian summer 1938. The blue haze of early fall veiled the snowy Sierra peaks that hem in the beautiful Fall River Valley. Mount Shasta, king of the Cascade Range, dominated the view to the northwest, while the queen of the Sierra, Mount Lassen, kept watch over the valley from the south.

It was fair and roundup time for McArthur. Horses and men of every known pedigree (and some that weren't known) had invaded this mountain cow town. Livestock, culinary achievements, and handiwork had all been judged and the rodeo was attracting the main attention. Bill Lee, a local cattleman and champion horseman in his own right, was ramrodding this western spectacle. Raised in this northwestern country on a large cow spread, Bill had the nature and the background to cope with horses and men that followed the rodeo sport. Then, too, his handsome appearance and pleasing personality coupled with a robust physique and a full knowledge of rough and tumble fighting were fine qualifications for a director of this western drama. In his prime no cowboy ever crowded him twice. His reputation was known far and wide as a fair and competent arena boss.

In those democratic days, horses used to try the contestants' skill were assembled from nearby ranges and ranches. No professional buckers were used. All animals were rounded up a few days before the show and were given numbers and names depicting their agility, color and disposition—Pit River, Juniper Jim, Yellow Fever, Black Bart, Bloody Island, Hounds of Hell, Swamp Angel, and Snake Eyes were some of the tough buckers back in those "new deal" thirties.

Bronc riders of note and fame were Perry Ivory of Alturas; Jack Meyers of Red Bluff, Bob Lockee from the parched lands of Arizona; McKinley Machach, a native Paiute; and last but not least, Marshall Flowers from Cottonwood, the poison oak district of southern Shasta. All were good men with spur and saddle.

Riding in the finals for top money on this dusty, balmy Sunday afternoon were Flowers, Meyers, and Lockee. Judging this tough, fast-moving event were Bill Eldridge of Pittville; Bert Jensen, Susanville; Roy Owens, Red Bluff. At this stage of the show all attention was focused on Flowers and a horse called Snake Eyes.

Flowers was a handsome, black-haired twister, standing over 6 feet tall and weighing about 230 pounds. It was said that with a little luck he could contest any horse on the circuit.

Snake Eyes was a blood bay, (slim built) clean-limbed gelding. His head was large and flat with small, ugly eyes resembling those of a rattlesnake. A 44 brand was stamped on his left hip and a CI iron was burned deep on his left shoulder, indicating that he had had more than one owner. This horse had been raised in the desert sagebrush country of Winnemucca, Nevada. His conformation indicated that a large amount of Standard-bred blood flowed in his veins. Fred Andrews, a horse trader, had brought Snake Eyes to the Fall River country and sold him to W. J. Albaugh, a prominent Pit River rancher. Albaugh had attempted to break this horse to the harness, but he proved to be a kicker; the reason that Bill Lee had him in his bucking string. Snake Eyes had no reputation as a bronc but Lee reasoned that any kicking horse was a bucking horse. Marshall Flowers drew this horse to compete in the finals; as he was ahead on points, any average ride would bring him the coveted first money.

As Snake Eyes was driven into the bucking chute he started a kicking spree. Marshall grabbed his panther-tracked scarred saddle from the arena dust and tossed it up over the chute; the horse kicked even harder. Somebody eared the horse down and another cowboy screwed on Marshall's "chair." The flank rigging was put in place. While this was going on, Marshall was putting on his chaps and spurs in a measured precise manner. Lee looked over the bucking chute and ordered an attendant to pull the flank rigging up one more notch. Marshall settled down on the summit of Snake Eyes, pulled his hat down tight, took a deep seat in the old association saddle and said, "Let me have him." The gate flew open and this Nevada raised bronc came out of the chute like a scalded cat. He leaped high in the air and kicked high behind; in fact, so high that he almost tipped over forward. Marshall was spurring high in the shoulders at the same time waving at the grandstand. The next jump Snake Eyes swapped ends, and the third jump he repeated this maneuver in the opposite direction—that's when the big burly cowboy from Cottonwood and Snake Eyes parted company. Marshall bit the dust, a disappointed, angry cowboy. The tense crowd roared! They wanted Jack Meyers to win the money, which he did by making a spectacular ride on Yellow Fever, a bronc from the Little Valley country.

The show ended, the chutes were emptied and the alkali laden dust in the arena settled to the ground. Dusty, sweaty cowboys as well as cheerful spectators made their way into the Buckhorn, a corner saloon known as the "water hole" by the natives. As Marshall Flowers passed through this pub's open door where songs and witty stories crept through, he elbowed his way quickly to the bar and snapped, "Give me a double whiskey three fingers high on the rocks." Bill Albaugh, owner of Snake Eyes, said to Marshall, "Why don't you mix some water with that whiskey, drink it slow and easy and enjoy your drink?" Marshall answered by saying, "When I drink whiskey I want to feel the effects of it right now!"

Continuing, Bill said, "You had hard luck this afternoon. I guess you found that old bay horse of mine kinda hard to ride."

Marshall, in his gruff way replied belligerently, "Maybe you think I can't ride that ole horse." Bill answered, "Yes, Marshall, I think you can if you'd hang on a little!"

The gay crowd laughed!! Marshall gulped down another whiskey and turned to face the crowd; hitting the bar with his huge fist he growled, "I can ride any horse in them there corrals, contest style.

No one in that smoke-filled room, steeped with the odor of thirst-quenching liquor questioned Marshall's bronc riding ability. So on that autumn day in that little western town he was loser in the arena but champion at the bar.

America's hero.

Reflections While Standing Before The Lincoln Memorial

The Japanese cherry trees were in full bloom along Pennsylvania Avenue on that balmy, spring day in 1954 when I stood in humble silence and reverence before the Abraham Lincoln Memorial. A hush filled this beautiful temple of Greek design, and I could feel the power and strength of this outstanding American. The feeling gripped me hard and held me like a spell. As I gazed on this nationally known statue of rare and nameless marble, I thought about the career of this great versatile man. His face looks sad but deeply honest; it appears eroded, depicting the result of making difficult decisions and of carrying heavy responsibilities. His ill-fitting clothes seem to drip with melancholy. The atmosphere is sad, brooding and depressing.

I became thrilled and impressed as I pictured the panorama of his life from a mountain background, a Kentucky log cabin boy, backwoodsman, farm laborer, clerk, flatboat hand, storekeeper, captain, postmaster, surveyor, lawyer, representative and finally, President of the United States.

By living near the soil and with a close kinship to nature, plus the aid and encouragement of his stepmother, Sally Lincoln, he attained in early life the many virtues that made him great. I was pleased and full of pride as I thought of him as a schoolboy, reading all of the few books available and studying diligently by the dim flickering light of a fireplace. He was a leader in school, an excellent speller, reader, and writer, and his many essays attracted favorable attention.

I was elated and stimulated as I imagined him growing to manhood and passing the bar as a witty, shrewd and competent attorney. Here in the courtroom, as well as on the bench, he was often described as a vigorous, comprehensive and able reasoner.

He was an impressive speaker with exact, clear judgment. He was a staunch believer in justice and freedom, fighting long, hard and relentlessly for these American principles. When I imaginatively remembered him as a storekeeper, a surveyor, and as an officer in the United States Army during the Mohawk War, I was pleased and impressed with his honesty, engineering ability and patriotism. As I traveled down the muddy Mississippi River with him as a flatboat hand, I was amazed at his physical strength and endurance which was further emphasized by his capabilities as a rail splitter and a rough and tumble wrestler. I walked beside him through the narrow winding streets of New Orleans and enjoyed the sights and atmosphere of that old and colorful town. Here Lincoln attended a slave market and conceived a deep-rooted hatred for the institution of slavery.

I thought about his career in politics and of the famous and renowned debating contests with Steven A. Douglas, "The Little Giant." His theme, "A house divided against itself cannot stand," and "Let me die in the advocacy of what is just and right," reflected his strong and unshakeable character. All of this, together with his rare leadership, executive ability, great knowledge of a free government, his simple and approachable manner and his insight into the human heart amazed and overjoyed me.

I recalled his first love affair and was saddened and full of grief when I saw his youthful dreams all shattered by the death of his young sweetheart. I was shocked again by the memory of his mother's passing and saddened to know that it was Abraham who fashioned the wooden pins to construct her crude and simple casket. I was depressed when I thought of his married life marred by a nervous, ambitious, and hot-tempered wife. I recalled the momentous day when he walked into the White House and was assigned the great responsibility as President of the United States in one of the most difficult and critical times this free nation has ever known. I felt his apprehension for the people during the bloody Civil War. His desire to unite the states and free the slaves was so strong it seemed to echo among the pillars of this temple.

I sat with him as he signed the Proclamation Emancipation, which freed the slaves and brought new hope to the common man throughout the world. I stood beside him at Gettysburg, when he thrilled scholars and statesmen alike with his brief but profound speech when he stated, "This government of the people, by the people, and for the people shall not perish from the earth."

Here was a man among men standing almost alone for democracy, and justice. I worried with him over the task of locating desirable fighting generals and was amused by his statement concerning General Grant when told that the general was drinking too much. "If I could find out what kind of whiskey Grant drinks, I would send a barrelful to every other general in the field."

I shared with him the painful decision for General Sherman's successful and famous "March to the Sea." I saw his huge, broad shoulders relax when relieved of the great responsibilities of war as the astute and cultured General Robert E. Lee handed his sword to Grant acknowledging defeat. I followed his thoughts regarding the reunion of the states at the close of the aftermath of war and his plans for curbing hatred, greed, and jealousy by promoting love and loyalty among his people. The economic and personal wounds of the war had been deep.

I pictured him in his home as a perfect and splendid host. He was a loving and thoughtful husband and father. I was gratified with these fine American principles. I marveled at the manner in which he lightened the burden of others, especially the children, the widows, the wronged, the poor, and of his ability to look into the future. He had honesty and fairness for enemy and foe alike.

I was deeply saddened by his assassination and was shocked when thinking of the great loss his passing was to the entire world. He was a great humanitarian with a wealth of tender compassion, an able leader, forceful and convincing speaker, a champion for freedom, and for the rights and privileges of the common man. His theory of democracy is best expressed by the following. "As I would not be a slave, so I would not be a master. This expresses my idea of democracy. Whatever differs from this, to the extent of the difference, is no democracy."

I meditated several minutes thinking what the world would have been like had Mr. Lincoln lived a full life span. Would his actions and deeds have brought a better understanding and closer friendship among people in all walks of life? Would his leadership and sympathetic reasoning have knit all people closer together regardless of creed, color or religion? Had he lived, the problem of integration as we have it today would be more nearly solved; such was the strong influence he exerted on the population.

I glanced around the temple for the final time reading parts of his inaugural addresses and the last line of the immortal Gettysburg speech. I tried to think what Abraham Lincoln would have thought had he known this memorial was being erected in his honor. This humble, unassuming statesman would have deemed it unnecessary. Yet it stands as a constant reminder that in a free land such as America anyone, regardless of culture, background or training, can be President of the United States.

These were the thoughts that coursed through my mind as I gazed upon this beautiful shrine. As I reluctantly turned to go, a young, handsome, impeccably dressed soldier walked into the temple. He had seen much action for on his khaki blouse were many military decorations. He went immediately to the base of the memorial, knelt down and began to pray. This was a touching scene and I knew then that Abraham Lincoln who rose above his humble origin and environment to leadership and enduring fame was truly America's hero.

The Lynch Brothers - Three

Taming "The Leopard" — Walter Lynch, California Rodeo, Salinas, 1913.
Courtesy Mrs. Walter B. Gregory

It was past the center of May in 1927. Range grass had ripened and withered; all the hills turned brown. "Beef" shipping was all done, and now was Roundup Time on the "Nacimiento." Several socialites from San Francisco had arrived; including I. W. Hellman, owner of this rancho, and his brother, Fritz, several of their close friends and, last but not least, the famed and renowned Fred Bixby with his charming daughter, "Sister", a top cowhand in her own right. Other celebrities and visitors included Benny Lom, soon to be the All-American halfback for the Golden Bears of California; and also his friend Al Kaufman, a great guard on the same devastating gridiron squad.

Neighboring cattlemen, too, were on hand for this 10-day roundup; Walt Bonnheim from the "Adelaide" country, the Stockdales from Paso Robles, then the three Lych brothers from the "Tierra Redondo" section. Among ranch personnel ready and rigged for the big rodeo were Eli Wright, ramrodder for the Nacimiento outfit, Ed Burden, Charlie Didimore, John "Turkey" Rankin, all good hands with horse and rope.

But Walter, Don and Harold Lynch are the men of this story. They made a grand picturesque entrance to the Nacimiento headquarters as they rode in on their top cow horses, trailing a remuda of fresh ponies and a lead-pack animal with their bedrolls and gear. All three were tall in their saddles and were at home on their horses. Walter, the oldest brother, was fresh from the parched lands of the Mojave country in Arizona where he had been operating a cattle spread of his own. He had on the side recently passed the bar examination and was now a full-fledged attorney. He rode a good sorrel Arizona pony that carried many brands, typical of the southwest range horses. His was a double rigged saddle with large, flat horn and a low cantle, certainly a striking new piece of equipment for those days. Like other cowpokes out of the old southwest, his rope was tied hard and fast. His brothers, Don and Harold, were mounted on larger native horses, both animals carrying silver mounted spade bits equipped with rawhide reins and romal. From their saddles swung grass ropes, with Harold's coiled backwards, indicating to all who noticed that he tossed his loops from the southpaw position.

Having recently arrived from the north where the Spanish influence had not yet penetrated, I found these customs were new. I had been raised in Indian country where names like Shasta, Siskiyou and Modoc held sway, and our saddles were "centerfire"; and "green" colts were started with snaffle bits.

After the men placed the remuda in the corrals and unsaddled the stock, supper was served, followed by much visiting, card playing and much tall story telling. These three Lynch brothers stole the show and were soon dominating every conversation, whether it be about cattle, law, modern or ancient history, or politics, local or state.

That initial evening I learned from Eli Wright that these redheaded Irish cowboys were blue blooded pioneer California stock. Their mother, a school teacher, was a charming gracious lady with a formal training in education. The father, Henry Lynch, a tall, handsome, intelligent man — once a senator and long a cattleman — was known far and wide for his western hospitality. Eli pointed out that these Lynch men were all top cowhands, excellent horsemen, expert hunters, and all well trained in the manly art of self defense. Each was humorous, witty, and an excellent conversationalist. These fine manly qualities were ably demonstrated in the following days of the roundup.

Early the first morning all riders assembled in the large area in front of the bunkhouse. Fred Bixby was mounted on his famous bay "hipshot" horse calley Hippy. Smoking a large expensive cigar, Fred called the riders together and gave them instructions on where they were to ride that day and the "circle" each was to make. Cattle were gathered from the hills and draws, then assembled on flat areas where they were bunched and held by a portion of the cowboys. After the fire was built, the "irons" were heated and the calves roped and brought to the fire for branding, marking, and castrating.

Mr. Bixby held a contract with Mr. Hellman for purchasing any bull calves that he himself roped from the herd. Time was allowed for him to locate the outstanding bull calves. Then these were soon roped and the Bixby brand burned deep on their hides. In all of these operations, whether it be rounding up, doing the roping, the flanking or branding, the three Lynch boys proved the top hands, excelled by no one.

During the second evening of the roundup, Benny Lom, the great U. C. footballer, wanted to attract some attention for himself and steal some glory from the heros of this story. Here was his way in attempting to do so.

Walter and Harold Lynch were in their bedrolls on the bunkhouse porch. At dusk that evening Benny quietly slipped up and doused them both with a dipper of cold water. Simultaneously they both leaped out of bed like two scalded cats and gave hot chase to the fleet halfback, even though they were barefoot while he was well shod. With a daring smile on his face, Lom took off at top speed toward the old blacksmith's shop, over rocks and gravel. He appeared to be heading for a touchdown in a football game. The swivel-hipped halfback cleverly side-stepped Walter's bulldog charges and then, in an impeccable manner, stiff-armed the cowboy to the ground. He then laughingly teased and coaxed Harold to tackle him. Lom failed to realize that the Lynch boys were accustomed to uneven terrain and were well versed in rough and tumble fighting. While watching Walter regain his footing, Lom became careless and Harold, with a flying tackle, hit him from the rear. He was brought down in the gravel and rocks with a crushing tackle, then Walter, coming to Harold's aid, put on a hammerlock. Benny screamed in agony, "You're hurting my arm!" Yet Walter cinched it up a little tighter. They soon led the famed football player to the side of the big watering trough right in front of the bunkhouse, and there they proceeded to duck him in a complete and collegiate manner.

This episode somewhat dampened Benny's spirits for a time, but it definitely enlarged his knowledge of and respect for the customs and traditions of the cattle country. This aborted bit of horseplay, no doubt, proved of real value to him in a later year when he stood out as a hero on the gridiron in many games with his kicking and passing and outstanding running. It surely proved of special value to him in 1928, the day he tackled his teammate Roy Regels, who was running toward the wrong goal line in that famous Rose Bowl game against the University of Georgia.

The rest of the roundup continued in a well-organized manner. Some 1600 calves were branded. Each noontime a beef barbecue was served. Suppers were prepared by Mrs. Eli Wright at the ranch headquarters. At the close of the roundup each ranch owner and his outfit returned to his own home range, several driving their stray cattle to home pastures.

As the Lynch brothers waved good-bye and crossed the sand-laden waters of the Nacimiento with the horses and cattle, I said aloud to myself, "There go three of the most versatile cowboy brothers the West has ever known." They were at home in the saddle and could be equally well poised in tuxedos if entertaining guests at the Palace Hotel in San Francisco. Julius Trescony later so able described them as he said, "They are tough, rough men in the mountains, but always gentlemen in town."

Teamed With Science

Records make the difference — Walter S. Markham, Salinas, Calif.

When Walter Markham left the flint hills and Osage country of Oklahoma about a third of a century ago, he had a longing and a determined urge deep down inside to own a cattle ranch in the "Golden State." Even when he was a school boy playing end on his alma mater's football team, the livestock range, and grass country had a powerful appeal.

It was in the rich Salinas Valley of Monterey County, California, that this energentic, hard-working, vegetable broker and cattleman struck paydirt and his boyhood dream began to be a reality. This was in 1936. He immediately purchased the beautiful Rancho El Toro of 763 acres, part of a Spanish land grant. This picturesque piece of dirt lies about 10 miles southwest of Salinas in the famed Corral de Tierra section. His great desire then was to breed good, practical Hereford cattle and a few Thoroughbred running horses.

During the past third of a century, this real westerner has had the pleasure of breeding and producing some of the top-performing Hereford cattle in California. The foundation of his purebred herd was based on the California Rover Domino bloodline. These cattle were developed at the University of California at Davis by the late Professor H. R. Guilbert and Alex McDonald.

Walter Markham was the first breeder of purebred cattle in the U.S. to gather officially postweaning data on his bulls. He is a charter member of the California Beef Cattle Improvement Association and hosted the first annual field day for that organization. This was an educational meeting to further the cause of performance testing of beef cattle. He was the first breeder in California to compile official records on progeny testing his herd bulls which included preweaning and postweaning as well as carcass cutability. The preweaning and postweaning performance of Markham's calves had been among the top in the CBCIA program.

Under the old get-of-sire program sponsored by the University of California, Walter was one of the first cooperators. His "get" won two blue ribbons at this event at the Cow Palace.

In addition to the purebred herd, he operates a commercial beef ranch at King City. By using the top gaining bulls he produces in his purebred herd, these commercial cattle are some of the outstanding performers in the state, bringing him a premium price for weaner calves each year.

In addition to breeding cattle, Walter has bred, in a modest way, some top Thoroughbred horses. One of the most thrilling and exciting experiences of his life was having a $100 bill on the nose of one of his strong, stout-hearted running Thoroughbreds when he came under the wire, a winner at 40 to 1. He also bred Sir Mark, a grandson of Man O' War, who ran the fastest 1¾ mile in the U.S. in 2.57 1/5 in 1948.

For over 40 years Walter has operated a very successful vegetable brokerage business. During his heyday he handled from 4,000 to 5,000 carloads of vegetables per year in the Salinas and Imperial valleys as well as in the Phoenix area. He has an enviable reputation in the produce industry which was built up by honesty and fairness to all concerned.

Walter has cooperated with the Agricultural Extension Service and the Animal Science Department of the University of California on many field trials relating to efficiency of beef cattle production. These tests were on feeding and breeding of beef cattle.

He also donated five cows for the growth study conducted by the genetics department of the University and one Thoroughbred mare for the project to study methods of increasing the foal crop.

Walter and his wife Lucille have 3 lovely daughters and 14 grandchildren.

There is an old biblical saying that "One cannot serve two masters," yet Walter Markham operates two large, important, and complex businesses. How does he do it? By long, laborious hours of hard work, shrewd business deals, coupled with a scientific, practical, enthusiastic and optimistic approach to all the various and sundry problems. This is an equation that you might equal but you cant' beat. It is one that has made America great!

A top herd sire.

The Battling Cowman — Roderick McArthur, McArthur, Calif.

Courtesy Mrs. Harold Ritter

The Pride of Fall River Valley

On August 9, 1944, I stood grief-stricken and sad by the bier of Roderick McArthur, pride and joy of Northern California and especially Fall River Valley. As I gazed on his beautiful flower-draped casket on that calm summer day, I though about the career of that great, versatile man. Here under spreading trees of his widely-known home, hundreds stood in deep silence with bowed and bare heads, paying their last and loyal respects to their hero while I tried to recall in brief detail his full and useful life.

I struggled hard to think of him as a barefoot farm boy learning the ways of life from a noble Scotch family, people who were high in culture, and with character that comes only to those who live close to the soil. I pictured him as a schoolboy, a bright scholar, already a spirited leader mastering the three R's and later acquiring knowledge of science, literature and law in higher institutions of learning. I saw him in early manhood, as a success-ful contractor and builder in San Francisco, the city of wealth, beauty and fashion he loved so well. I saw him while his youth was still in flower, called back to the land to manage and pro-mote the John McArthur Land and Cattle Company successfully for over a decade. Here in his heyday with his brothers and the pick of the mountain men around him, great herds of cattle were established, tons of feed produced, many sections of crops grown, and thousands of acres of land controlled and developed. I saw him in hay fields when the summer heat would wilt most men, and on cattle drives when the north wind brought bliz-zards of snow and rain, yet he never faltered or complained, but instead gave encouragement to his helpers. I saw him in the courts, both high and low, where he fought savagely and relent-lessly against great odds, for what he thought was right and just for the interests of the common man. Here his bulldog courage, coupled with a wide knowledge of the law, usually won the favor of both judge and jury.

I saw him at rodeos, fairs and other community gatherings, leading, cooperating, always giving his best to make this old globe a better place in which to live. I saw him on hunting trips in the rugged hills and lava beds of White Horse, happy carefree, and entertaining, as only he could be, yet strong, big and bold as the mountains he loved. I remembered him at cattlemen's conventions where he orated and pleaded cooperation for the good and advancement of that old and colorful industry. I liked him in his home as a perfect generous and entertaining host, and with his wife beside him and his children at his knee, as a loving and thoughtful father and husband. I enjoyed hearing him counsel with a troubled friend and later saw the bewildered friend take on new courage, hope and faith. To the ill, the injured and the crippled, his words of encouragement were healing and soothing.

Imbued with that pioneer spirit and conviction that only the deserving should be blessed and that no one should get anything for nothing, Roderick lived a full, generous and unselfish life. A great untiring community worker, patriotic, a firm believer in freedom, Roderick was truly an outstanding man in his field during his generation.

I thought as I stood there that I should rather have lived a life such as his—siding with the children, with the weak, with the poor and with the wronged than to have climbed all the ladders of life that ordinarly man attempts to scale, where all the good things Roderick McArthur stood for are pushed aside by the cold hand of ambition and greed.

And if I were to propose a toast to this cattleman, I would say, "Here's to Roderick McArthur, powerful, rugged and true, generous, loving and big hearted, a real Westerner, the salt of the earth, a regular all-around champion."

Versatile Rambo

A money ride — Gene Rambo on "Try Me", Eureka Rodeo, 1949.

There is a saying among rodeo contestants that a top bronc rider never becomes a champion roper—or vice versa—and that all good bucking horse riders come from the Northwest while winning rope slingers hail from the Southwest. Around the cattle circles, men say that a renowned and famous cowboy never becomes a successful cattleman.

Gene Rambo, cattleman of Shandon, California, a native son of the golden state, astute, tight-twisted, modest and easy going, shattered all of these precedents. To prove this statement, Gene spurred and dallied his way to four all-around world cowboy championships in the International Rodeo Association—at the same time operating a ranch and building up one of the top cow herds in California. This is a feat that no other cowboy has accomplished and is a record that will probably stand for a long, long time.

Starting at the tender age of 17, Gene entered his first rodeo at Cambria Pines where he took second money in the bull riding contest and earned $37.50. (At that time he was riding colts on the Estella Ranch for $35.00 per month.)

This win spurred him on and for the next fifth of a century he took part in approximately 900 rodeo contests from as far north as Calgary, southwest to the Lone Star state of Texas, and east to New York and Boston, the cradle of U.S. history and culture. He showed his versatility and strong competitive spirit in this spine-chilling sport by entering in six events at most of these shows. He tackled bronc, bareback and bull riding, calf and team roping and last but not least, bulldogging. During his long and colorful "moon lighting" career, he earned over $200,000 and managed his ranches at the same time. He traveled to these shows mostly by automobile but for some he took to the air, flying rented planes. He estimated that his costs for traveling, entry fees and other expenses were about $100,000. He received no fringe benefits for being supreme champion except a $1,500 award given by Levi Straus Company.

Gene did not particularly specialize in any one of these six events. He tried to be the top man in all of them. In other words, it was a thrill for him to win the bulldogging event as well as to put on a supreme display of horsemanship on a "sun-fishing" bronc. The most difficult horse that the Shandon rancher ever forked was called "Wild Swede." The "Swede" was a big horse weighing about 1,400 pounds, a head slinger that kicked moderately high behind—but most of the time sidewise. Other tough bucking horses were, "Scene Shifter," "Big Enough" and "Golden Rule. During his prime he rode every horse on the circuit and was bucked off in the bronc riding contest an average of 1½ times per year and only 3 times from a bareback horse. This is a record that comes to few people.

During his rodeo career, Gene trained to keep in shape by taking exercises and doing road work. This kept his legs in condition and improved his wind. He didn't smoke, drink, or carouse around. He was dead serious about this rodeo business and was in it to win—a tough competitor when the chips were down. Because he was always in excellent shape he had very few injuries during the 20 years of stiff competition. He didn't say so but it's assumed that the "Man Upstairs" looked after Gene while he was participating in those dangerous contests. His most serious injury came while he was doing ranch work. One of his horses fell and broke Gene's femur. While roping an old dairy cow he got the third finger on his right hand caught in the rope and pulled it off.

When asked if he had any fights while rodeoing, his answer was, "I didn't have time. I was always too busy. When you take part in six events you don't have time even to think about getting hurt. You're concentrating on beating that other guy." This star rodeo performer didn't pretend to put on any showmanship acts. He did the best he could, followed the rules of the book to the letter, and hoped the judges were honest. Most of the time they were. Among some of the best riders during Gene's career were Casey Tibbs, Deb Copenhaven, Louis Brooks and Fritz Truen.

Speaking of roping, Gene had this to say, "A well-trained horse is over half the battle. He has to be a smooth runner, doing his best each day, and in the calf roping must put pressure on the calf by keeping a taut rope. The hardest part of team roping is catching the heels. Most of the time this was my assignment.

"In 1958 I decided to cut out the rough stuff of rodeoing completely and hang up my 'rig' and spend most of my time and energy building up my cattle herd on my two ranches. Then, I met a young man by the name of Jimmy Rodriquez who was an excellent roper and was dripping with talent to catch horns. I coached him a little and we teamed up and during the years of 1959, 1960 and 1962, I won $21,590 and Jim won $26,215."

Continuing, Gene said, "I have quite a few young boys who come to the ranch for help and instructions, particularly on roping. I am always glad to help them when I have time."

He was asked, "Why don't you start a school where you could train young teenagers in the science and art of rodeoing?" He answered by saying, "I have often thought of this and I think it might work. My ranch is a little remote for such a school but I do think it would help the teenage delinquency problem."

"You were a high school dropout, Gene, Why did you quit your formal training?" he was asked. He replied, I got bored and didn't want to be pushed around and didn't want to be told what to do. Furthermore, I had future goals that I wanted to reach. The lure of the rodeo had a magnetic urge. If I were a teenager today, I would probably join the wild bunch."

He said this and laughed and then had his 2½ year-old grandson recite the "Pledge of Allegiance to the Flag." This indicates surely that Gene is a solid citizen. He said, "This fellow is going to be my future roping partner."

The same fierce great will to win that Gene Rambo displayed

while in the rodeo arena is now being transferred to improve beef cattle production. He is a staunch member of the California Beef Cattle Improvement Association. He believes in accurate, complete records on every animal on the ranch. He reasons this by asking, "Why guess, when you can measure performance with the scales, ruler, microscope and computer?" His lovely and gracious wife, Barbara, assists in his record keeping.

Marion Stanley, livestock farm advisor in Monterey County, works closely with Gene on his ranch management. Marion has a Ph.D. degree in Animal Breeding from the University of Wyoming and helps in planning and analyzing Gene's cattle breeding program.

Nine years ago this wideawake cattleman started a crossbreeding program and begun artifically inseminating his cows with semen from the "highest producing" bulls available. When the first crop calves were born, everybody thought that this was a practice way out in left field. When he bred these F-1 heifers to a purebred bull of another breed, then "they all knew he was crazy." Today, crossbreeding is a widely accepted practice where efficiency of beef production is desired.

This former all-star cowboy is an exception when it comes to employing artificial insemination. He has a record of having a conception rate for a 21-day breeding period of 68 to 86 percent. (The reason he likes artificial insemination is because semen from the highest performing progeny tested bulls is available. This hastens breed improvement faster than with ordinary bulls.

At weaning time each Rambo calf gets a million units of Vitamin A and the cows 2½ million. This is administered intramuscularly. He feels that this treatment reduces incidence of pink eye and increases fertility. Gene "bird dogs" for the American Breeder Service and has secured several herds in which he assists in inseminating the cattle. The most underestimated part of artificial insemination, according to Gene, is detecting cows in heat. In order to do this correctly, much experience is required. This progressive, positive-thinking cattleman has designed a chute for artificial insemination breeding. Blueprints and specifications have been developed at the University of California for this structure. Anyone interested in this chute should contact his farm advisor. Artificial insemination has another advantage in that it fits in well with crossbreeding programs. Only one herd needs to be maintained.

At the present time, Gene is doing a little investigating into some of the exotic breeds such as Limousine and Simmental. He is concerned about the fertility of beef cattle and is developing a program where he can select for this trait. Although fertility in beef cattle has a low heritability, he is of the opinion that if disease and the environment can be controlled in a herd, selection for regular reproduction can be attained.

It is his belief that in the next 10 years, attention to fertility in beef cattle will occupy the interest of not only scienists but also beef cattle producers. In this regard he is particularly excited about the Simmental breed. He feels that this strain of cattle not only will add gaining ability to the offspring but also will put meatiness in the carcass and pump fertility to the breeding herd. Rambo is disappointed in many cattlemen's attitudes about improved practices. He feels too many are reluctant to change because they are afraid to meet and face up-to-date challenging methods. He reasons that a majority of those producing the beef steaks today are running their herds similar to the way they did 30 years ago.

In discussing grading standards for carcass beef, Gene is of the opinion that too much emphasis is placed on marbling and that the meatier carcass will be more in demand in the future. In this regard he is high in his praise for yield grading. "The trouble with the cattle business," states Gene, "is that everything is based on averages." When this system prevails, the cattleman who produces the high cutting carcusses is penalized while the mediocre beef gets a premium even though it is below average. Yield grading will help to change this picture.

This year, 1970, Rambo sold his steer calves for 35c a pound on the ranch without any shrinkage. During the past several years his heifer calves have been sold for replacement purposes, bringing all the way from 4 to 7 cents a pound over the market price for feeder heifers.

Gene served as team roping director for 5 years for the Rodeo Cowboy Association. His hobbies are hunting, fishing, breaking horses, and training dogs.

As I left the Rambo's spacious home, which is laden with hospitality and friendliness, and overlooks beautiful Cholame Valley hemmed in by chamise covered hills, I said to myself, "Gene Rambo is the greatest, most versatile all-around cowboy who ever lived. With his tough, scientific approach to the improvement of the beef cattle business, one can predict with a great degree of accuracy that in the not too distant future he will be qualified to be crowned "Dean of Cattlemen."

As Julius Trescony, well-known cattleman of San Lucas, California, often said, "In all my travels, I can't recall meeting a man with more God-given talents than Gene Rambo. Here is a top bronc rider, champion roper, excellent cook, superior marksman with rifle or shotgun, an expert hunter, a fine host, and a progressive cattleman who thinks like a scientist and has the ability to put results of research to work."

Yes, versatile Rambo, the highest compliment we can pay you said in good old cow lingo is, "We would all like to ride the river with you."

A typical California Spade bit.

The Pace Setter

Scientific cattleman — Jack Rice, Alturas, Calif.

Up north in the Modoc Country, historically rich in cattle and Indian wars, Jack Rice is known as the cattleman who puts science to work. Working with former farm advisor, Norman Nichols, this hustling cowman was the first in California to scientifically select his replacement heifers at post-weaning on rate of gain and grade, two highly heritable traits that enhance the efficiency of any cow herd.

The same fierce aggressive desire to win that he demonstrated on the resin of the boxing ring canvas is now being extended to beef cattle production. Jack pioneered systematic programs on crossbreeding of beef cattle. For example, on his 850-cow herd he is crossing Angus and Herefords, Polled Shorthorns and Angus. He is doing some investigational work on the value of Charolais in the crossbreeding program. He has found that these crossbred cattle have a higher percent of calf crop, and the calves are heavier at weaning. In order to increase weaning weights farther, his cows are bred to calve in January or February rather than March and April. This program alone has increased weaning weights a "whopping" 50 pounds.

He successfully breeds his heifers at 15 months of age, calving at two. This program increases percent of calf crop and puts black ink in the ledger.

This wide awake cattleman has built a maternity ward to "lamb out" these heifers. Jack is a pace setter. This past year he launched an artificial insemination program, using Charolais and Simmental semen. The results of this program will be watched closely by this positive-minded cattleman.

Jack has constructed a working horseshoe shaped cattle chute. This piece of equipment is so constructed that cattle move in and out with a minimum amount of labor and at the same time reduced shrinkage. The University of California has developed blueprints and specifications for this structure which are available through your county farm advisor's office.

A Stanford graduate in political science, then two years at the University of California at Davis studying animal science make up Jack's formal training. While at Stanford, he was on the boxing team for four years and was captain during his senior studies. He won the Gene Tunney trophy for his outstanding accomplishments in the "Squared Circle." During and after college, he engaged in over 100 amateur fights and refereed professionally in this sport for six years. No man ever crowded Jack twice.

He enlisted in the Navy during World War II and was discharged as a lieutenant commander. Most of these war years were spent in the jungle-clad harsh, tough South Pacific.

In 1949, Jack and his vivacious and ebullient wife Kitty deserted the concrete canyons and the society social whirl of San Francisco and headed for the tall timber of Humboldt County, to manage the Pacific Lumber Company's cattle operations near Scotia. Here the Rice family was very active in both the Cattlemen and Wool Growers Associations. The P. L. ranch hosted several beef cattle educational meetings while Jack was the manager.

With an urge to own their own business, they invaded Modoc County in 1954 and started in the cattle business by buying the Wall Ranch; later the Floyd Allen property; then the Leoni Ranch, giving them a total of 5,800 deeded acres. In addition to this, the Rice Cattle Company which is composed of Jack, Kitty, two sons, Mike and Tom, and daughter, Sally, have grazing rights on U.S. Forest Service and BLM lands.

Jack's hobbies are team roping and scuba diving. He takes an active part in Modoc County Cattlemen activities and is prominent on Republican political committees.

The Rice home is steeped in generosity and friendliness. As in the days of old, their doors are open wide for those who chance to pass along the way. Theirs is truly pioneer Modoc hospitality.

Prominent Modoc Cattlemen.

Promoting the March of Dimes — Governor Knight and Don Smith,
Red Bluff, Bull Sale

The Man Behind the One in Front

Don M. Smith, well-known county director and livestock farm advisor, emeritus, of Tehama County, and I sat reminiscing in the old Crystal Motel at Red Bluff. It was bull sale time and bulls and men of every known pedigree were invading this old and historical cow town. Don was enthusiastic, relaxed, jovial, ebullient and anxious to cooperate in relating the details of his full and useful life.

To those in the know, Red Bluff, Don Smith and the bull sale are synonymous. You cannot talk about one without thinking of the other; they ride the range together, stirrup to stirrup.

I stretched my imagination to picture Don as a barefoot boy in the corn fields of Iowa, where already he was developing that rare and intangible trait called character that comes so often to those who live close to the soil. I pictured him with his shiny dinner pail, "piking" off to school with Henry A. Wallace, former vice president of the United States and secretary of agriculture, under the F. D. Roosevelt Democratic administration of the New Deal 30's.

I imagined him mastering the three R's through grade and high school, already a spirited leader and a brilliant student. I followed him through Iowa State College where he majored in animal science, working his way through the institution by managing a laundry. Studying lecture notes of top students in various subjects allowed Don to skip classes, but he passed these axaminations with flying colors.

In 1917, Don married Margaret Frazer, who was at that time secretary to the dean of the School of Veterinary Medicine, Iowa State College. Don and Margaret raised four children — Don A., Dick, Jean and Marcia. All four are following successful, worthwhile careers.

He enlisted in the U.S. Army and distinguished himself in Flanders' Fields during World War I, the war supposed to end all wars. It was here that he helped crush the German army and then added life to the song that was so popular, "Over There." Upon returning, he successfully managed several large ranches in southern California. Here he supervised one of the largest Duroc Jersey hog ranches in the United States.

I saw him enter the Agricultural Extension Service in 1921 and under the guidance and stimulation of B. H. Crocheron, then director of the Agricultural Extension Service, he became one of the most effective farm advisors in all the western country.

It was in Stanislaus County that he began as an assistant farm advisor. Here he organized a cow testing association of over 5,000 cows with the help of many important people including Carl Wente, banker and later president of the Bank of America; Sam Greene of the California Dairy Council; and G. Eddy Gordon, that renowned first Extension dairy specialist. It was here Don learned that when you have people helping voluntarily you give them the credit. "Giving credit to the other fellow is like bread cast upon the water; it comes back a thousand fold," he said.

He was transferred to Tehama County as the first farm advisor in 1923, and I watched him working with the cattle and sheepmen during the dreaded hoof and mouth disease epidemic in 1924. Here he assisted inspecting more than 70,000 cattle and 200,-000 sheep. I saw him organize the first olive conference, which resulted in an increase in county appropriation and paved the way for the appointment of Grant Merrill as assistant farm advisor. The Smith-Merrill team was compatible and effective in teaching and research, and built an excellent Extension program.

He worked with farm youth, 4-H Club boys and girls, the most important crop in Tehama County, and trained them in the improved practices of agricultural leadership and good citizenship. Under Don's regime and guidance, Tehama County produced more senior 4-H members than any California county.

I saw Don establish feeding tests with hogs and sheep to prove the value of adding protein to their diet. Don was the first California farm advisor to demonstrate the value of balancing barley with high protein feeds (such as meat scraps) in livestock rations. He organized and promoted the Tehama Livestock Marketing Association, an organization that was successful for years in selling 8,000 to 10,000 hogs annually, and bringing thousands of dollars of added income to farmers in Tehama and surrounding counties.

Also in the field of marketing, Don was instrumental in helping to organize the Valley Livestock Marketing Association at Red Bluff. This organization markets hundreds of head of beef cattle each year, performing an important service to the beef cattle industry in California, Oregon and Nevada.

I admired his full utilization of the resources of the University of California and his close cooperation with the Animal Science Department. Here distinguished men like George Hart, Elmer Hughes, Bobby Miller, Jim Wilson, and Bill Regan were extremely helpful in carrying out his many and varied Extension activities.

I watched him as secretary of the Northern California Wool Growers' Association where he lectured and pleaded for cooperation and unity among the sheepmen of that area. With the help of Chet Wing, secretary of the California Wool Growers' Association, I saw him organize the strong and influential committee for the control of predatory animals. For his untiring efforts on behalf of the sheepmen, he was chosen as a member of the Order of Golden Fleece.

Ray Anchordoguy, prominent sheepman of Tehama County, stated that Don Smith took him out of a sheep camp and made him a sheepman instead of a sheepherder. When Ray took over the management of his sheep ranch, the average weaning weight of the lambs was approximately 80 pounds and percent of lamb crop was 90 percent. With his management and Don Smith's assistance, the precentage of lamb crop was increased to 140 percent and weight of lambs to 95 pounds.

In 1924 Don organized the Tehama County Dairy Herd Improvement Association which encompassed Tehama, Shasta, Butte and Glenn Counties. The average milk and butterfat production at that time was 6,500 and 260 pounds, respectively. In 1946 the average milk production among Tehama County herds had increased to 8,500 pounds and butterfat production to 340 pounds. This was due to culling, use of high-producing bulls, and better feeding practices which Don demonstrated and advocated. A conservative estimate indicates that this project alone added over half a million dollars annually to the Tehama County farm income.

I remember him judging all classes of livestock at county and district fairs and livestock shows. This is a great and versatile accomplishment that comes to few men.

I saw Don training young personnel in the most effective manner in which to carry on Extension work. By example, he taught them to be courteous, thoughtful, and well-mannered. He encouraged them to be punctual, to remember names, to be up-to-date on subject matter, and to be forceful and entertaining as speakers. He showed them the value of the written word and the importance of being the man behind the one in front. He encouraged them to be specialists in some field of agricultural production. Those he trained and who later were county directors included: Frank Smith, Ben Ramsaur, Carl Rimbey, John Underhill, Lester Berry, Harry Hinkley, and Leland Frey.

It was stimulating to watch Don Smith counsel with a confused and depressed farmer and then see this tiller of the soil take on new hope and courage in his struggle for success against the elements.

In his home Don was a generous and entertaining host and a thoughtful and loving husband and father.

In his heyday, he organized the popular and unique Red Bluff Bull Sale. For some 20 years, with the help of the Bull Sale Committee (Sam Ayer, Sidney Watson, Roy Owens, Charles Stover, J. T. McKerras, Charley Luther, and L. H. Rochford, first livestock specialist), he promoted, organized and expanded this worthwhile, far-reaching event. He introduced the University of California grading system into the sale in order to improve the quality of the consignments. He called this sale a buyer's event rather than a breeder's sale. He and his committee did everything humanly possible to protect the buyer, and this made the sale famous throughout the U.S. During the 20 years that Don managed the Red Bluff Bull Sale, approximately 7,000 head of big, rugged Red Bluff-type bulls were sold. Estimating that these bulls increased weaning weights of calves by 20 pounds and that they produced 80 calves in a 4-year period, this meant an increase of 11,200,000 pounds of beef. At 30 cents a pound, this amounted to over $3 million in added income.

A big feature at this sale was the selling of the "March of Dimes" bull. This event raised more than $135,000 for this worthy charity. He originated a unique selling system for the March of Dimes by inviting special honorary auctioneers, such as Tennessee Ernie Ford, "Pappy" Waldorf and the late Max Baer, who was the best of them all in Don's opinion. Don's best gimmick for promoting this sale was the initiation of a special section of the Red Bluff Daily News dedicated to feature articles on beef cattle prepared by county agents and livestock specialists and producers throughout the West. This special feature gave much publicity to the sale.

We were together when he organized the Tri-County Cattlemen's meeting at the Charley Stover ranch in Chester, an event that is still popular with cattlemen. Here he demonstrated without a doubt that bulls graded at the Red Bluff Sale and used on the range for three years or more, maintained the same grade as when sold. This meeting did much to convince cattlemen that visual evaluation such as grading was a highly repeatable practice when performed by skilled and trained judges.

He organized the Sacramento Valley Irrigation Committee and with the help of James K. Carr, Bureau of Reclamation and many others, the Sacramento Valley canals became a reality. He testified before congressional committees in Washington on the value of increased irrigation in Northern California. He worked closely with Governors Knight and Warren, emphasizing to them the importance of the Sacramento Valley canal system which included Red Bluff Diversion Dam and the Trinity Dam recommended by "Californians for the Trinity." I saw him receive the pen with which President Truman signed the bill legalizing the Sacramento canals. This was presented to Don by the late Senator Clair Engle.

As Don stood on the banks of the Red Bluff Diversion Dam and watched the snow-laden waters of the Sacramento River diverted into the parched lands of Tehama County, one could clearly see a gleam of satisfaction and pride in his eye. This activity was the big one — a job well done.

Few people have built worthwhile, important monuments reflecting their own accomplishments in the field of agricultural improvement. It was the miner in the Golden Fifties with his pick, pan and shovel that put Red Bluff and Tehama County on the map. But Don Smith's scientific and educational programs in agriculture and related civic activities have spotlighted this old and colorful cow town and county in great style during the past third of a century.

As I sat talking to him, I thought "Here is a man who successfully championed the cause of the cattleman, sheepman, other farmers, and the farm boys and girls in making life on the land more abundant."

To propose a toast, I would say, "Don, you sat tall in your old battle-scarred Extension saddle; you cast long shadows in the field of education; your furrows of community activities were straight and long. Your loops of scientific knowledge were thrown straight and true. As an organizer and promoter, you have no peer. Your enthusiasm and competitive spirit are contagious and stimulating. You are a man among men — a champion in the corral as well as on the platform."

The oldest cattle trade mark — Spanish AT, Julius Trescony, San Lucas, Calif.

A Cattleman to the Very Last Degree

One of the most widely known, popular, friendly and successful cattlemen in California is Julius G. Trescony of San Lucas, Monterery County, California. A native son of the Golden State, Julius represents the cattleman and the West in all its entirety.

He was born during the Gay 90's on the Rancho San Lucas Grant and has spent his entire life in that area. His grandfather, the late Alberto, accumulated this property in the early 1840's and this ranch has been in the Trescony name for over one hundred years, encompassing five generations of Tresconys. Its adobe buildings, Latin landscape, friendly and hospitable owner, and the entire atmosphere depicts the carefree days when Spain ruled California and fiestas and siestas were the rule of day — truly the last of the old-time Spanish haciendas. Julius' office contains many antiques, such as pictures, ranch equipment, and written documents together with the Spanish **JC** branding iron said to be the oldest registered brand in continuous use in California.

Alberto Trescony was a native of Italy, and was a tinsmith by trade. Upon landing in Monterey in May, 1842, he made tin cups and pans for the miners and being astute and frugal, he not only accummulated Rancho San Lucas but also the Chupinos and Tularcitos Land Grants in Carmel Valley.

Julius received his early schooling in the San Lucas area and graduated from the University of Santa Clara at the age of 18. He was one of the youngest graduates from that University with a bachelor of arts degree.

He learned to be an expert horseman from his father and in the early days participated in many of the rodeos in Monterery County, including the California Rodeo and Salinas. Here he was champion trick rider for two years and also won the team roping with Walter Lynch from the Tierra Redonda country as his partner. He boasts of having missed only one day of the California Rodeo since its inception in 1911. During the 1967 show Julius was honored by the Federal Land Bank for his many contributions to the livestock industry

In 1920 he married Marie Griffin, a neighboring cattleman's daughter. Marie and Julius raised three sons, Louis, Mario, and

Julian. Louis, a graduate of the University of Santa Clara with a degree in electrical engineering, does research at the University of California in Berkeley. Mario attended Cal Poly in San Luis Obispo, and Julian graduated from the University of Santa Clara with a degree in business administration. The two latter sons are in partnership with Julius on the ranch.

In 1928 Julius bought out the heirs of the Trescony family and became owner and manager of Rancho San Lucas. At that time this was a diversified operation, including the raising of cattle, sheep and hogs as well as barley. When he acquired this property, it was heavily in debt, and Julius at that time weighed 133 pounds dripping wet, and often said he owned more per avoirdupois pound than any man in California. Operating a cattle ranch during the New Deal Democratic 30's and carrying a heavy debt was a tough and difficult assignment.

Creditors were nipping at the heels of many ranchers throughout California and the West and foreclosures were not uncommon. Through hard work, good management, and help from close friends Julius was able to survive the depression era and paid off his debt.

Two years ago 1800 acres of rich mesa land on the Trescony grant was put under irrigation and is now producing row crops such as sugar beets, beans, peppers, tomatoes, and garlic. This is said to be one of the largest private irrigation developments in California. It shows the foresight of Julius when he retained the water rights on the Salinas River so that his former barley land could be converted to the production of high-priced crops.

Water to irrigate this land is pumped a little over two miles. It is stored in reservoirs and applied to the land with sprinklers. This is a Spreckles Sugar Company development project under a lease arrangement with Julius and his sons. The rest of the ranch is devoted to the production of beef cattle. Replacement heifers are selected on a scientific basis using post-weaning rate of gain and grade, two highly heritable traits.

Rancho San Lucas was always kept clean, spick-and-span, fences repaired, and buildings maintained and painted. When asked why he kept his ranch looking so neat, Julius stated, "When the sheriff comes after her, I want him to be proud of her."

The Trescony ranch has been used for many years as a small experiment station by the University of California Agricultural Extension Service. Numerous field tests on many varieties of cereals, range grasses and legumes have been conducted. Results of these experiments have been helpful in establishing approved productive varieties of these plants for use in other areas of the state as well as Monterey County.

Julius was the first cattleman in California to practice systematic crossbreeding of beef cattle. He was also one of the first to successfully breed heifers at 15 months of age to calve at two years. It was here that he observed that crossbred heifers came into sexual maturity sooner and have less calving problems than did those of straight breeding. These observations were later documented by research work conducted at several experiment stations.

The value of supplementing dry range and/or barley stubble with a high-protein feed such as cottonseed cake was first demonstrated on the Rancho San Lucas. These results had far-reaching effects in encouraging other cattlemen to incorporate this profitable practice into their management operations.

Julius grew the first Mariout seed barley and also pioneered the growing of certified seed under the Cal Approved program. The malting barley grown on his ranch became known as "Trescony" barley and for many years was exported to England for manufacturing a high-quality beer and ale. Each year when selling this premium barley Julius sold it for top price with a new pair of cowboy boots thrown in "to boot." This contributed in part to his reputation as the best dressed cattleman in California.

His ranch is a favorable meeting place for educational and demonstrational gatherings on new practices in agronomy, range improvement, and animal husbandry. The eradication of brush and scrub trees from the range on a large scale was first introduced by Julius. He developed a roller to crush the brush and after it was dried, by the use of fire, the debris was eliminated. Then by the use of a disc plow and a root ripper, the land was prepared for the growing of barley and grass. The Trescony ranch practices in range improvement stimulated others to adopt similar measures, thus leading to still greater improvements.

Julius invented an adjustable cattle branding chute, a wire gate fastener, a float valve for watering troughs, a cattle guard, and a branding iron stove. Plans for this equipment were included in a University of California Bulletin entitled "Beef Handling Equipment," thus passing on this knowledge to other cattlemen.

During his long active and useful life, Julius has been very prominent in community affairs. For thirty years he served as school trustee for his local district. He was one of the first directors of the Salinas Valley Fair in King City and for many years was chairman of the 4-H and Future Farmer livestock auction sale. He introduced the calf and lamb scramble at the King City Fair.

The lamb scramble is for girls only, and the Salinas Valley Fair is the only place this event is held. These events not only provided entertainment, but were helpful in securing animals for livestock projects.

He was one of the first directors of the California Cattlemen's Association and was president of the Monterey County Cattlemen's Association. He has been an active member of these two organizations for many years. He served as president of the Monterey County ASCS program when it was known as the Triple A organization. He is a member of the Monterey County Farm Bureau and has taken part in many of its educational activities.

For many years Julius served as chairman of the restoration committee for the Mission San Antonio near Jolon. Due to his efforts large sums of money were raised to repair this old historical edificio. For years Julius solicited tons of food for the Saint Anthony's Dining Room in San Francisco, he was a member of the founding Board of Directors for the George L. Mee Memorial Hospital in King City.

This colorful cattleman can speak five languages, namely, English, Spanish, Italian, French and Basque. This is an accomplishment that comes to few men and it enabled him to serve with distinction during World War I in Navy Intelligence. He has traveled widely having made two tours of Europe and has visited several Latin American countries.

His knowledge of horses and horsemanship was utilized when he was asked to judge cow horses at the California Rodeo and at the Sacramento State Fair. While appraising these animals at the State Fair, he noticed one large Palomino with a peculiar movement of his tail. Upon investigation, he found a large chunk of lead securely and secretly tied in the hair. This was to prevent the horse from switching his tail. On discovering this, Julius asked the owner to take his horse back to the barn. The owner became quite indignant and asked if he could show his horse before the crowd that evening. Julius replied, "Yes, you can show him, but I will announce that you are doing so with a chunk of lead in his tail!"

During his youth Julius broke many good cow horses California style. These horses were started in the hackamore, then gradually worked into the double rein and finally finished with a spade bit. This method when properly executed resulted in a horse with a velvet mouth and excellent rein. One of the best was a sorrel horse called Chapo. He was not only an excellent cow horse, but could also jump hurdles. To show how well mannered Chapo was Julius rode him into a bank in Salinas during "Big

Week" without a saddle or bridle, cashed a check and rode out. This is discipline to the 'nth' degree. This horse had confidence in his owner.

One of Julius' favorite expressions is "Never hurry in the hills." Another is "Poco a poco se anda lejos," which means little by little you travel far. He often said, "Give me men that are rough and tough in the mountains, but always gentlemen in town."

Julius is a great admirer of Don Smith, former manager of the famous Red Bluff Bull Sale. Julius made this statement, "When better bulls are sold, it will be at the Red Bluff Bull Sale." He stated the only reason Don Smith was not manager of the Burnam and Bailey Big-Time Circus was because they had not heard of him.

Julius is one of the most optimistic and positive thinking individuals that anyone would want to meet. Quite often when the rains failed to come and it was very dry—here was his philosophy: "You cannot make rain when you want it, you cannot stop it when it starts; hence, if you are that helpless, why worry? In fact, the energy spent worrying should be utilized more constructively." Julius would tell his friends, "Everything is going to be all right. You must have faith!" He would then make a bet that the Salinas River would run under the bridge at Soledad by March 25. He often won these wagers!

In 1969, he was chosen livestock man of the year.

A few years ago he lost the sight of his right eye. But he did not complain; he was only thankful for having the use of it for over seventy years. He proceeded to remodel the sights of his rifle and shotgun and continued to hunt. This is optimism—a wholesome, positive attitude! An avid hunter, he is an expert with rifle and shotgun, and an authority on the habits of the game he hunted. Most of all, he enjoys the conviviality of the friends who hunt with him.

Julius is a top hand with horse and rope. He takes his dallies in the dark. He wears the western hat, and colored shirt, the blue jeans, the high heel boot and the jingling spurs with flair and distinction. He is equally at home in a tuxedo.

Yes, he is a real cattleman, a true westener—to the very last degree.

The author telling it like it is — Humboldt County Cattlemen's meeting.
Courtesy John Dunbar

Is Your Answer Yes?

The disparity between beef prices and what cattlemen pay for goods and services is real and disturbing. How cattlemen can receive a larger share of the housewife's dollar has puzzled this industry for the past decade. Many different solutions have been advocated to increase bargaining power such as voluntary orderly marketing; integration; cooperation among all segments of the industry; intelligent use of up-to-date market information; and supporting beef promotion programs.

In reviewing this problem it might be well to review the manner in which the price of beef is established. It is simply SUPPLY AND DEMAND. This supply-and-demand picture may seem extremely complex, because it is not easy to determine how such a mechanism operates. Let us inspect the demand side of the business. The consumers' purchasing power (the amount of money set aside in the housewife's meat budget) often controls demand. On the average, about 5% of the family's income goes to buy meat. Since consumer income does not change much from day to day or week to week, the same number of dollars stretches over a larger meat supply when cattle marketings are increased. Supplies are larger in relation to income. When this happens meat prices usually go down.

There are many factors that determine what the housewife must pay for beef, such as competition from other meats and proteins which replace beef, seasonal habits, weather, and religious beliefs.

Each cattleman has his own ideas concerning the number to produce and where and when to sell. Because so many different decisions are being made, great variations of market prices result. Factors that cause these fluctuations are: weather conditions (heat, cold, snow, rain, droughts, floods), holidays, feed supplies, and opinions of how and when to market. Beef is generally moved to the consumer within ten days after slaughter. It is a perishable product and only about 3% is stored. There is keen competition between the 3,000 packers, 10,000 commercial killers, and over 300,000 retail stores. Due to this, the middleman has very little effect upon setting the price a producer receives or a consumer pays.

The packer, wholesaler, and retailer do have certain responsibilities. They must operate their business efficiently. This being done, retail prices can be made more attractive to the consumer, and the lower the price, other things equal, the greater the amount of meat consumed. The middleman, especially the retailer, can create more demand for beef by using up-to-date merchandizing methods, leading to conveniences in buying. These include attractive packaging, a polite and courteous attitude, advertising, and advice on preparing certain cuts for cooking.

Each cattleman has certain responsibilities in his own field of production in helping to solve this price-squeeze situation such as increased efficiency. If he can answer "yes" to the following questions, he should then turn his attention toward cooperative effort in order to receive larger bargaining power.

1. Are you using plus-gaining bulls? By this, do you buy bulls with official records, and is their lifetime gain to 15 months of age 2.25 pounds per day or more under good environment? Do these bulls have the modern conformation—long bodies and legs, wide and thick in the round, heavy forearms, clean in the brisket and flank, showing plenty of masculinity about the head, neck and genital organs, structurally sound in feet and limbs?

2. Do you semen-test your bulls? This should be done each year by a qualified veterinarian approximately two months before the breeding season. Bulls showing poor-quality semen should be retested in thirty days. If semen is still of poor quality, they should be sold.

3. Do you have your bulls gaining in weight a month before the breeding season?

4. Do you rotate your bulls during the breeding season? That is, do you turn half of them in with the cow herd for the first ten days, remove them, and put in the other half for a similar period? This is a profitable practice.

5. Do you keep production records on your cow herd? This is the only sound and sure method of determining high-producing cows in the herd and locating the culls. There are several organizations that perform services on processing records for beef herds. Among some of them would be the State Beef Cattle Improvement Associations, Production Regis-

try International, and several breed associations. When individual records are kept on a cow herd, it stimulates better management by the owner and affords him a basis on which to improve both genetic influence and environment of his animals.

6. Do you cull low-producing, old, crippled, poor udders, and shy breeders each year?

7. Do you have your cows gaining in weight approximately one month before calving and until the breeding season is over, which is usually about three months post-calving? A considerbale amount of research evidence is available which shows that animals kept under this type of nutrition program come into heat sooner and the conception rate is higher. These animals also have higher milk production which means heavy weaning weights.

8. Do you breed your heifers at 15 months of age weighing 600 pounds or more? Research work indicates that cows bred to calve at 2 years produce about 1 calf more during a lifetime than those bred to calve for the first time at three years.

9. Do you pregnancy-test your cows 60 days after bulls have been removed from the herd? Since it costs about $75 a year to maintain a cow, this is a profitable practice. It also eliminates hard and shy breeders and increases percent of calf crop.

10. Have you fully explored the possibility of using artificial insemination (AI) in your management? Semen from superior bulls can be used to increase weaning weights and grades of calves, and it eliminates the money invested in bulls. More and more commercial cattlemen will be using AI with proper management, such as nutrition and care. Beef cows can be artifically bred for the first 25 days of the breeding season and you can then use pickup bulls, to settle the remainder of the cows.

11. Are you taking full advantage of crossbreeding? Research data indicates that production can be increased by 10-15% by crossbreeding. Best results are secured by the use of a cross-bred mother, selected on official records. Crossbred cows have a higher conception rate, calve easier, live longer, and give more milk than do the straight-bred animals.

12. Do you have a controlled breeding program? That is, in the northern areas have all your calves come early in the spring, during a 90-day period. This is more desirable than running bulls with the animals year-around and producing a non-

uniform calf crop as far as size and age are concerned. In most southern areas early calves (October, November and December) are most economical to produce. The reason is that these animals are old enough when grass becomes available on the range to take full advantage of this feed, which would not be the case with late calves.

Some cattlement in the mountain areas are seriously considering the production of fall calves also. This system cuts down the number of bulls that are used; animals can be bred at home where crossbreeding can be practiced; and cows will calve in areas that are more free from diseases, which is conducive to raising a larger percentage of calves. Work conducted at the experiment station in Burns, Oregon, indicates that the fall calf is considerably more profitable than the spring-raised calf.

13. Do you feed your calves after weaning for continuous growth? It has been definitely proven by many experiments that calves supplemented on the range with a high-protein feed, such as cottonseed cake or fed through the winter so they will gain about one pound per day for continuous growth after weaning is a profitable practice. For every dollar spent on feed during this period, they return about $2. Such a system also makes it possible for the growing out of heifers so that they can be bred at 15 months of age.

14. Do you select your heifers on rate of gain and grade? Rate of gain, following weaning until the animals are about 15 months of age, has a heritability of about 60%. Grade, which is the conformation of an animal, has a heritability of about 30%. After weaning, animals should be individually weighed, fed for continuous growth, gaining about a pound a day, and selected for breeding based on these factors—*growth rate, grade, structural soundness* and *fertility.*

15. Do you make a thorough study of the marketing situation? In other words, do you study market reports, converse with cattle buyers and feeders on market outlook?

16. Do you keep updated on cattle numbers, weather conditions, and the purchasing power of the consumer?

17. Do you ever consider owning your cattle until they are in the hands of the packer, rather than selling them as weaners or yearlings? Those cattlemen who produce reputation cattle— fast gainers, high graders, high carcass yielders—should consider going all the way with these animals. This system has a double-barrel effect in that the owner can take advantage of

the built-in rapid gain and also the increased effect of the use of stilbestrol to add to the efficiency of production. There are several hundred custom feedyards in the country that can feed animals for individual cattlemen.

18. Do you sort your cattle on age and grade before offering them for sale?

19. Do you show them to the buyer in clean, desirable surroundings?

20. Do you cooperate with local marketing organizations when selling your cattle? This usually increases your bargaining power.

21. Do you encourage yield grading of beef carcasses; thus securing a premium for high cutting cattle?

22. Are you a member of your local and state cattlemen's associations; and do you sponsor beef promotion programs?

23. Last but not least—do you have an up-to-date disease control program? Do you vaccinate your animals for the many different diseases which vaccines can control? Your policy should be "prevent" rather than "cure." Proper nutrition and disease control will go a long way in protecting your animals?

If you cannot answer "yes" to the majority of these questions, your only alternative is "use your crying towel."

High producing crossbred cattle on Sexton, Eidman Ranch.

Courtesy Monte Bell